S

PERSPECTIVES IN APHID BIOLOGY

A. D. LOWE *Editor*

BULLETIN No. 2

THE ENTOMOLOGICAL SOCIETY OF NEW ZEALAND (INC.)
c/o Entomology Division, D.S.I.R. Private Bag,
Auckland, New Zealand

PRINTED AT THE CAXTON PRESS
CHRISTCHURCH NEW ZEALAND

CONTENTS

34497

FOREWORD

In September, 1972, the Entomological Society of New Zealand held its twenty-first conference at Lincoln College, near Christchurch, New Zealand. This conference was planned to follow the Fourteenth International Congress of Entomology held at Canberra, Australia, and thus be open for attendance by an international audience. With the agreement of the appropriate authorities of the International Biological Programme, the New Zealand conference was planned to include a meeting of their Committee on Biological Control of Aphids. Plans were therefore made to include in the Conference programme a symposium on aphid biology and to consider some broad questions associated with this topic.

It was appropriate that such a subject be considered at Lincoln, since this area has in recent years become the centre of aphid research in New Zealand, largely through the work of a team of scientists engaged in the study of aphid biology and ecology, virus diseases, and the search for resistant plant material.

The committee organising the symposium realised that all aspects of aphid biology could not be covered in the time available. The choice of topics was limited to some extent by available speakers, but it is interesting to note that in a final discussion, participants were agreed that three aspects only lightly touched on in the symposium were the very points at which further research is urgently required. These were: flight, especially the question of the origin of alates landing in fresh crops and whether they have arrived from near or far; predators and their activity within an aphid population; and the use of plants resistant to aphids, especially whether such strains could be used with suitable predator activity to replace the regular use of costly chemicals as a control measure.

At the conclusion of the conference, which was attended by more than two hundred delegates, it was agreed that the papers offered should be published, and that they should be preceded by an account of aphid studies by New Zealand workers.

The Entomological Society of New Zealand agreed to sponsor such a volume and offers it as part of its 21st anniversary contribution to the science of entomology.

A. D. LOWE
President

APHID BIOLOGY IN NEW ZEALAND

By A. D. Lowe

Entomology Division, Department of Scientific and Industrial Research, Lincoln, New Zealand

INTRODUCTION

The standard work on aphids in New Zealand is a monograph by Cottier (1953). Largely taxonomic, this volume was born of the need to understand the biology of aphids because of their importance in agriculture. They are possibly of equal significance in horticultural crops and the cultivation of ornamentals, but these plants are frequently subjected to sprays for various purposes, and it is little trouble to add a suitable aphicide to an already continuous programme of pest control. Agricultural crops, however, usually offer a much lower per hectare net return. In such crops a single application of a chemical for an occasional problem is reasonable within the cost-profit structure, but the continuing nature of aphid-virus problems on susceptible crops calls for less costly approaches. The frequent application of sprays to these crops is simply too expensive. Apart from the cost of materials in repeated sprayings, application is frequently only possible from the air in such crops as cereals, a process which adds further to the cost. Such considerations have necessitated an alternative approach to control under New Zealand farm conditions.

Crop rotation — major crops

In general New Zealand agriculture is aimed at maximum per hectare production of animal products from sown pastures, mainly ryegrass-clover mixtures. Such areas total eight million hectares, at elevations up to 600 metres, and are favoured with a temperate climate. Approximately ten per cent of such areas is ploughed each year and sown in crops. These crops offer the grower a quick cash return or suitable winter stock food. They are brassicas, cereals, potatoes and legumes, and all have aphid-virus problems. The importance of understanding the biology and ecology of aphids in these crops has been the reason for most of the work undertaken in this field in New Zealand.

Minor crops

Aphid and virus problems affect a number of crops in New Zealand other than those listed. Carrots are regularly infested by *Cavariella aegopodii* (Scop.) and suffer from motley dwarf virus (Smith et al, 1969). Western celery mosaic is known in celery crops in some parts of the country. A number of aphids are known in small numbers from the Umbelliferae but *C. aegopodii* is the one which regularly infests celery. There are few umbelliferous weeds in the country's flora and it is thought that continuous growing of celery is a main contributor to epidemics of this disease. Tomatoes and lettuce are colonised regularly by aphids in some districts and it is considered that aphid-borne viruses are of some importance in lettuce crops. Symptoms of cucumber mosaic virus are common in many plants. The aphid *B. helichrysi* (Kltb.) has regularly colonised experimental crops in the family Compositae, such as sunflower and safflower. Perennial experimental plantings of peppermint are colonised by the aphid *Ovatus crataegarius* (Walk.). Strawberries are troubled by the strawberry aphid *Chaetosiphon fragaefolii* (Cock.) which can be kept in check by pre-flowering sprays. It is notable that hops and tobacco are grown in the Nelson area without any sign as yet of serious aphid-borne diseases.

Cottier (1953) listed 59 species of aphids in New Zealand. These included a number of cosmopolitan species, several of which are non-specific in their plant host preference, and six species quite rarely seen which he described as endemic. Two of the latter group were from single records. Further work has now extended the list to more than 80 species, with the addition of one further possibly endemic species, not yet described.

From about 1935 work on aphid resistant brassicas has been carried out by plant breeders but since 1957 several workers have in addition been engaged in the study of the biology and ecology of aphids and viruses, and the introduction of new species of predators. This work has resulted in a reasonable control of several problems using a number of different methods.

APPROACHES TO CONTROL OF APHIDS AND VIRUSES

Resistant Plants

Brassicas: Palmer & Smith (1967) listed the fields in which selection and breeding were then taking place — brassicas, carrots, peas, tomatoes, cereals and potatoes — but it is in brassicas that this work has its longest history in New Zealand, and its greatest claim to success. In the other crops listed considerable tolerance to aphid-virus attack is evident in some varieties, but brassicas of several types which show resistance to both aphids and viruses are now available to growers of commercial agricultural crops. Results from a replicated experimental field planting sampled by Lowe (Anon. 1961) are shown in Fig. 1 and indicate that the total aphids (*Brevicoryne brassicae* (L.)) on 30 plants sampled at the end of 120 days growth showed a ratio of 50:1 on susceptible and resistant rape. The resistance is noticeable during vegetative growth but is not maintained during the reproductive stage. The ecological implications of this fact are discussed later in this chapter.

Alteration of sowing date

Cereals: In cereal studies Smith (1963) demonstrated the presence of barley yellow dwarf virus in New Zealand wheat crops and also showed that the application of a single chemical spray to wheat could increase yields by up to 20%. This was interpreted as indicating that virus damage was being increased by secondary spread. Most wheat in the area is sown in the autumn and a study of aphid incidence in early sown fields showed that the main vector was *Rhopalosiphum padi* (L.), and that alates of this species landed on young plants almost as soon as they emerged in autumn-sown crops, usually during May or in seasons favourable for late flight, in early June. Examination of the detail of flights of this aphid led to the establishment of an aphid warning service, operated by interested Government agencies and Lincoln College. The service operated over four seasons and the detail of its operation has been reported by Lowe (1967).

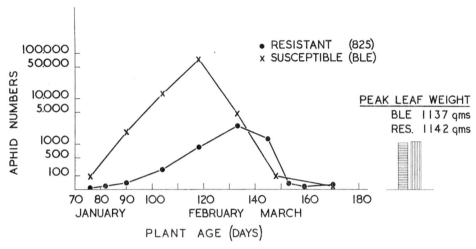

Fig. 1 Comparison of total *B. brassicae* on 30 plants of susceptible (BLE) and resistant (825) rape, in replicated plots (6 reps. x 5 sample plants) at Lincoln, 1960.

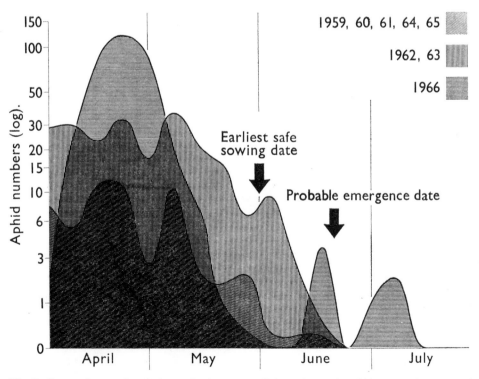

Fig. 2 Composite graph of the end of autumn flights of cereal aphid *(R. padi)*, grouped according to years. This is the information used to determine a "safe sowing date" for autumn-sown wheat in New Zealand.

9

In addition to the regular trapping at three sites on the Canterbury Plains a further 18 single traps were operated by advisory officers or in a few cases by willing farmers, over several seasons. Data from the tail of the flight pattern gave clear indication that in 9 out of 10 years, flights ceased at all observation points by the end of June. Ninety per cent of flights had ceased by mid-June. A general recommendation therefore to sow wheat after the beginning of June (Fig. 2) was substituted for the warning service, and has remained a feature of wheat growing advice since. This avoidance tactic appears to have solved the virus problem, and is accompanied by advice on the use of chemicals for those who find it impossible (e.g. on heavy land) to follow the preventive planting advice.

Carrots: Examination of the detail of flights of the carrot willow aphid *Cavariella aegopodii* (Scop.), showed that its flight incidence was much greater in spring than in autumn. This appeared to offer opportunity for a similar avoidance strategy. The problem of carrot motley dwarf virus had been examined first by Smith et al (1960), but suggested chemical remedies are costly and take insufficient note of the susceptibility of this crop to off-flavours. The problem was also commented on by Close (1967) and later examined by Lowe (1971), who reported that damage-free carrots had been grown over several years by late planting to avoid the vector. The basis for such avoidance procedure is clearly shown in the flight curve (Fig. 3).

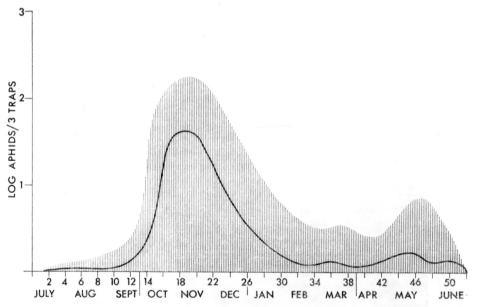

Fig. 3 Generalised flight pattern of the carrot aphid *(C. aegopodii)*. The shaded area represents overall range of numbers trapped, and the black line the mean, taken from 21 annual sets of data from three trapping sites in Canterbury. The data emphasises the peak flight in spring (cf. Fig. 5).

Use of granular insecticides

Potatoes: Driver (1965) stated that useful resistance to potato viruses X and Y had been incorporated in new varieties. Potato leaf roll virus remains as the outstanding problem in this crop. The production of virus-free seed and its relation to virus spread within the crop are main considerations in the problem of control. The cosmopolitan aphid *Myzus persicae* (Sulz.) has been shown to be the effective vector. Work by Close (Rough & Close 1965) using systemic insecticide granules beneath the soil at planting time has shown this method to be effective (Fig. 4) without undesirable side effects of chemical sprays such as causing mortality among predators and parasites. Up to 90 days effective control has been shown to be possible giving disease-free seed for use in the following year, and increasing yield of table grades of potatoes by 15% in the year of application.

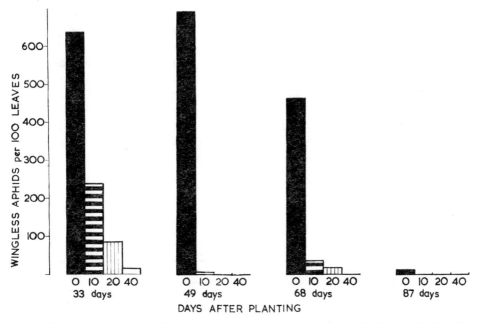

Fig. 4 Counts of wingless aphids on potatoes, when planted with 0, 10, 20 and 40 lbs. of a granular insecticide (5% a.i.) per acre; indicating effective control of early infestation by aphids, and prevention of subsequent virus spread.

Use of chemical sprays

Cereals. The control of *Macrosiphum miscanthi* (Tak.) in cereal crops is achieved by the use of systemic insecticides from the air. Current work on this insect is more fully recorded later in this chapter.

Peas: This crop is occasionally treated with chemicals for aphid control, although the problems associated with aphids and viruses in peas are not yet fully understood.

Palmer & Smith (1967) recorded developed resistance to pea mosaic virus, and the problems of spread of pea leaf roll virus in spring-sown pea crops is currently under investigation. It appears, at this stage, to call for examination of vectors, the main one at present suspected being *Aulacorthum solani* (Kltb.) which is known in some seasons to overwinter on Lucerne (*Medicago sativa* L.) As legumes such as clovers (*Trifolium* spp) are an important component of New Zealand pastures, and are periodically infested by a number of aphids, the problem

11

requires widespread investigation. Other aphids known to infest legumes are *Aphis craccivora* Koch, and *B. helichrysi*. Wilson & Close (1972) have examined the infection of pea crops with subterranean clover red leaf virus, and demonstrated that here, too, *A. solani* is the main vector.

RECENT APHID STUDIES

Trapping

In 1957 the need for a better basic knowledge of aphid incidence led Close and Lamb to initiate a trapping programme at three sites across the Canterbury Plains, an area of over a million hectares, rising from sea-level to almost 500 metres, situated on the eastern half of the South Island. The programme was serviced from Lincoln and aimed partly at adding to the existing knowledge of aphids on potatoes and brassicas, both of which are widely grown in the area. The following year a parallel programme to examine the population dynamics of *B. brassicae* on brassica crops was launched by Lamb & Lowe and the trapping work incorporated in this programme. Results of these studies have been reported by Close & Lamb (1961), and Lamb & Lowe (1961, 1967). The population study continued at three sites for three years, and the trapping study lasted ten years. Results have been far reaching and were published by Lowe (1968a). 51 species of aphids were trapped, nine of which flew regularly in high numbers, and have been referred to as primary species. They are listed in Table I.

TABLE I

PRIMARY APHID SPECIES IN CANTERBURY

Numbers trapped at Lincoln and Annat, 1959-66, in decreasing order of total catch.

Species	Autumn	Spring	Total
Brevicoryne brassicae (L.)	50,295	16,023	66,318
Myzus persicae (Sulz.)	5,152	1,092	6,244
Rhopalosiphum padi (L.)	1,602	3,084	4,686
Cavariella aegopodii (Scop.)	164	3,447	3,611
Capitophorus elaeagni (del Guer.)	2,360	420	2,780
Aulacorthum solani (Kltb.)	457	2,240	2,697
Lipaphis erysimi (Kltb.)	415	624	1,039
Brachycaudus helichrysi (Kltb.)	106	455	561
Macrosiphum euphorbiae (Thom.)	75	148	223

The species *C. elaeagni* is of no importance in crops, its succulent host plant being thistles, mainly *Cirsium arvense* (L.) Scop.

Interpretation of trapping data

When such data as the above are listed weekly by species it is possible to make important interpretations relative to species biology and control. For instance, the avoidance tactics used in making recommendations for aphid control in both cereals and carrots arise directly from the data taken weekly from traps. Comparisons for consistency of incidence between sites, species, seasons and years are readily available. When plotted as flight patterns the data are self-explanatory where education of growers is involved.

Populations on plants

In New Zealand, studies of populations on plants, combined with testing of alates from plants for infectivity, has shed considerable light on the problems of aphid-virus spread. Wilson and Close (1972) reported on the study of subterranean clover red leaf virus by this method. An insistence among plant-breeders that potential lines of plants developed for various purposes be tested under unprotected field conditions has meant the development of broad tolerance to many disease problems. Cereals for instance, developed in New Zealand, all show reasonable tolerance to aphids and the associated BYD virus.

The field study of aphid populations on plants has not offered the same biological rewards as has trapping of aphids, but it has confirmed that generally populations on plants follow much the same pattern as that demonstrated in flying aphids (Fig. 5). This basic population pattern has also proved useful in the study of parasitic organisms.

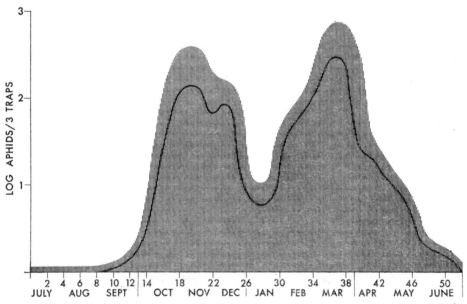

Fig. 5 Generalised flight pattern of crop aphids in New Zealand, derived from three main species flying *(B. brassicae, M. persicae,* and *R. padi).* Shaded area shows overall range of numbers flying, and black line the mean, of three species over 63 sets of annual data.

Biological control

The parasites and predators in New Zealand aphid populations have been recorded by Valentine (1967). These studies, and the work reported by Lowe (1968b), have resulted in a decision to introduce further predators to supplement existing biological control organisms. These are two Coccinellids *Coccinella septempunctata* L. and *Oenopia sauzeti* Muls., and the Chrysopid *Chrysopa carnea* Stephens, and are at present under study in field situations prior to general release.

Entomophthora spp

A number of species of entomophthoraceous fungi have been recorded on aphids in New Zealand, and the results of field observations of their incidence on *B.*

13

brassicae have been recorded by Lowe (1968b). The incidence of these diseases is usually low in spring and high during warm humid conditions prevailing in the autumn. Occasional outbreaks occur in summer in high density aphid populations but generally speaking disease is absent when it would most greatly assist in control. No work has been undertaken on artificial dissemination of such diseases. These fungi are found on all species of aphids of economic importance with the exception of *R. padi* and *M. euphorbiae,* the latter species being low in incidence on traps and in crops, but the most prolific aphid taken on ornamental plantings in home gardens. *M. rosae* on roses in home gardens also appears to be unaffected by fungous diseases in spite of high density populations which develop regularly on this host.

CURRENT WORK

The problem of *Macrosiphum miscanthi* (Tak. 1921)

This aphid was recorded from New Zealand by Cottier (1953) under the name *M. avenae* (Fab.). He stated it "had not yet proved of economic importance in this country." Eastop (1966) stated his conviction that it was more correctly named as *M. miscanthi* (Tak. 1921), and further indicated that though similar to *avenae* of Fabricius, it was probably the tropical variety of that species, and could be shown to be morphologically distinct. Though only a single alate was recorded during the 10 year trapping programme, during the summer of 1966 specimens were recorded from plants at several widely separated points. In the following years, after trapping had ceased, major populations of this aphid species were taken on plants in spring, and wheat crops throughout the country were heavily infested. It has been a problem on developing heads of cereals regularly since that date. (Lowe, 1969).

There are a number of important ways in which its ecology differs from that of *R. padi*. It appears to be of no significance in late autumn when the wheat plants are emerging. This may be due to its flight habits differing from those of *R. padi,* or may possibly be related to its lesser efficiency as a virus vector (Smith et al, 1968). Sanderson & Mulholland (1969) reported on trials with chemicals for the control of this aphid, and indicated several further important differences from *R. padi*. The main incidence of damage in wheat was from flights when the plants were in head. Alates colonised the developing head and caused lowering of seed set, as well as shrinkage of individual grains, giving heavily reduced yield. Chemical examination of the grain showed considerably heightened alpha-amylase levels and increased protein content. Baking tests revealed a deterioration of crumb structure.

Wheat crops sown in spring in the North Island suffer similar damage, as well as a different pattern of infestation by *R. padi,* and work in the control of these aphids has been reported on by Blackmore (1969).

These reports emphasise the fact that at this stage *M. miscanthi* is the one aphid on crops the only control approach to which is through chemicals. It is fortunate that a single well-timed spray of a reliable aphicide if efficiently applied by aircraft, appears to give adequate control. This is probably because the crop, once it is in head, rapidly passes out of the stage where it is attractive to flying aphids, so reinfestation does not occur. But field observations also indicate that

14

predators, particularly coccinellids, are present in high numbers in these crops and must suffer severe damage if the crop is sprayed. The aphids are also affected by *Entomophthora planchoniana* Cornu but not early enough in the season to reduce their density effectively.

Current research using clones

The recurring nature of the problem of *M. miscanthi* has led to the initiation of further lines of basic biological research, using aphids from cereals, under controlled conditions at Lincoln College. While not at present suggesting direct leads in non-chemical methods of control, these studies are likely to revise some of the concepts which have been accepted not only about New Zealand aphids but to some extent about parthenogenetic aphids in general. Data from this work will not be available until the present series of experiments is completed but already some facts are clear from preliminary results.

When three species of aphids from cereals were brought from the field and raised as clones, and then subjected to short-day treatment (10 hours daylight), it was found that each species showed its own particular response when raised on homozygous plant material (Arawa Wheat F16 et seq.) at a series of temperature regimes.

A species of *Macrosiphum*, probably a strain of *euphorbiae* was taken in mid-autumn (April) on *Zea mays*. Without further treatment, it yielded a line of nymphs from a single female in which one out of four individuals continued as a viviparous female, giving rise through several generations only to similar forms. Three out of four individuals were oviparae, one of which deposited parthenogenetic eggs on wheat. Normally strains of *M. euphorbiae* taken from plants such as *Dianthus* spp continue throughout the winter as parthenogenetic viviparous females. This result shows that this strain had already undergone field treatment to produce sex forms.

When clones of *R. padi* were subjected to 10 hours of daylight using 16 hours as a control, at temperatures of 15.5° and 12°C no sex forms were produced, even when exposed to this treatment for 15 generations.

A clone of *M. miscanthi* similarly exposed to a 10 hour day at temperatures of 15.5° and 12°C gave rise to some males at the higher temperature, at a mean level of 0.5% of the population after six generations of treatment. At the lower temperature, a small number of oviparae were also produced. Segregated rearing of progeny from individual sexuparous parents showed that several types of adults were present. The sex forms are red or reddish and can be easily distinguished, even before birth. Some sexuparae gave birth to a few or no male nymphs, even though these could be seen to be present in the parents. A few sexuparae gave birth to 15 to 20 males, probably a normal potential birth-rate for this form. Others gave birth to a few males, and then reverted to production of normal, healthy, viviparous females. The majority of the population, exceeding 99%, though exposed to exactly the same treatment throughout and before the experiments failed to produce anything but viviparous females, even after exposure to short-day treatment for up to 15 generations.

Several wild populations of the same species gave much the same level of production of sexual forms when exposed to the same treatment as a check. All experiments were conducted with parallel specimens exposed to the same

15

conditions with a long-day regime (16 hours daylight) as controls. These colonies, both clonal and wild, continued to produce only viviparae.

This work has an important bearing on three questions associated with New Zealand aphids.

1. Origin of New Zealand economic species

Economic species affecting crops are prolific, having probably 15 or more generations a year in the parthenogenetic viviparous form. Two important exceptions to this are *M. persicae* and *C. aegopodii,* both of which have two parallel populations in winter, one on the secondary succulent host-plants and another as eggs on the primary woody host. Up to the present it has been suggested that European man has introduced most of the cosmopolitan aphid species through trade in plants and produce. Following the work of Johnson (1967) in reporting on dispersal of insects along meteorological pathways, there has been increasing credence given to the concept of inter-continental, possibly even global, dispersal of flying aphids. At the present time such a theory lacks definitive evidence, but studies in an isolated area such as New Zealand, and such evidence as has been collected by Wise (Cottier, 1964) from the Campbell Islands, and by Horning (unpublished, 1970) from the Snares Islands, both south of New Zealand, and only rarely visited by man, suggests the possibility of wind dispersion. This could explain the periodic plague appearance in New Zealand of an aphid such as *M. miscanthi,* possibly drifting from Australia.

The testing of *R. padi* under controlled conditions, and the failure to produce sex forms is strongly suggestive of one of two possible explanations. One is that the absence of the preferred host-plant, *Prunus padus,* (Dixon, 1971) has screened from the population those individuals with a potential for reproduction of sexual forms, leaving over a period of one hundred years or so since man settled in New Zealand, only those clones suited to anholocycly on Gramineae. An alternative explanation would be that the species has invaded New Zealand naturally and originates from stock in tropical areas north of New Zealand, where the sexual forms are also unknown. Hence its form cannot be changed by exposure to a short-day regime.

The acceptance of the latter explanation for the presence of not only this species but also the many species in New Zealand known only in the viviparous form, leaves room for the suggestion that where parallel strains exist which overwinter as eggs, these are probably from colonies brought to this country from Europe in the normal course of settlement, and have retained the egg-laying propensity, since man has also introduced the appropriate host-plants.

2. Occurrence of sex forms in New Zealand

Another widespread opinion in New Zealand which calls for closer examination is that the day-length does not reach the lower threshold required for precipitation of the change in aphids to sex forms. This concept is untenable, however. Lees (1966) in summarising the available evidence states that the threshold required to induce the change is just over 14 hours, whereas in New Zealand the shortest day is around 10 hours daylight including 9 hours of sunlight. Days below 14 hours daylight occur each autumn. These facts suggest further evidence in favour of a

16

tropical origin for those species in which no sex forms normally appear under New Zealand conditions.

The production of consistently low numbers of the sex forms in *M. miscanthi* on exposure of both clones and wild populations to short-day conditions, is a phenomenon that does not fit any of the known patterns of reproduction, and calls for further investigation, especially since the results appear to be repeatable in different populations and at different temperatures.

3. Fitness in aphids

Other forms of variation within clones are evident in New Zealand aphids. In previous studies (Lowe 1970) the variance within clones is shown by analysis to be greater than that between clones for the different factors studied, such as generation time, birth-rate and total life span. This suggests a highly adaptable organism, and is probably the explanation of the fitness of parthenogenetic aphids. In New Zealand such strains are among the most successful of insects, and though no explanation is at present forthcoming for the genetic mechanism behind such variation and prolificacy in an asexual organism, the facts seem to deny the oft-repeated statement found in standard texts that parthenogenesis represents "an escape in a phylogenetic blind alley" (Dobzhansky, 1951). Stebbins (1938) similarly states "An agamic complex is a closed system. It can give rise to nothing new".

The established variation within clones in New Zealand in a parthenogenetic aphid rather supports the work of Cognetti (1961) who coined the term endomeiosis to indicate his belief that some type of exchange within meiosis was the pathway by which such variation probably came to pass in the parthenogenetic aphids with which he worked. Whatever be the genetic explanation of the facts, they suggest highly adaptable species, and this is reflected in the considerable success of these forms of aphids as colonising organisms in the New Zealand agricultural scene.

FUTURE RESEARCH

It remains to consider what may be the most profitable lines along which further research in New Zealand could result in better control of aphid virus problems in agriculture. *B. brassicae* is still the most prolific aphid in New Zealand if the position is judged by numbers caught on traps. This aphid usually constitutes two-thirds of the catch. In spite of the number of available lines of brassicas which show good resistance during the vegetative stage, an ecological view of the problem would suggest striking at the aphid popuation when it is at its lowest ebb, in winter, and thereby preventing its early spring build-up (Fig. 5). At present no resistance is available in brassicas during the reproductive stage, and hence crops kept for seed become the means by which the population is maintained from year to year in agricultural plantings. The introduction of aphid resistance in the reproductive stage of the plants would be a major achievement, and would be likely to contribute to better control of this species by reducing the potential for build-up of an early spring population.

New Zealand is not well supplied with biological control agents for aphids. The current work in introducing further general predators is soundly based but could well extend to an examination of mass rearing by any means including the use of artificial diets, and the testing of mass releases of predators in infested crops. This would require to be associated with extensive quantitative studies to establish the benefits or otherwise of such "flooding" techniques, but would be well worth the effort involved.

A field of knowledge which needs further enquiry is the flight and landing of aphids, with a view to establishing the sources from which populations of alates have transferred. A basic enquiry of this nature would probably be more rewarding than field population or aphid trapping studies aimed at establishing correlations with various factors operating intraseasonally, such as weather. The present state of knowledge of the source of flying aphids in New Zealand, as elsewhere, could well be summarized in the words of Johnson (1962), "It is not possible to tell where invasions come from, and the aphids seen flying on still days may have come from the next field or from 100 miles away". The solution of this problem by the examination of gut contents, by serological techniques, or the estimation of fuel reserves in landing aphids, possibly by labelling, may well tax the ingenuity of the next generation of New Zealand aphidologists. Some indication of its solution will mean a considerable advance in ecological knowledge, for there is little evidence from which to make deductions at present.

A further study of two problems which at the moment do not lend themselves to control except by chemicals, is at present under way. These are the control of the grain aphid *M. miscanthi,* and the investigation of the viruses and vectors affecting legumes. Active research programes are at present under way in an endeavour to add these problems to the list of those which have been reduced in severity in New Zealand agriculture by an approach based on sound knowledge of the biology and ecology of the aphids concerned.

TABLE II
APHID AND VIRUS CONTROL ON CROPS IN NEW ZEALAND

Crop	Virus**	Vector	Control Recommended
Brassicas	Cauliflower mosaic	*Brevicoryne brassicae*	Resistant
		Myzus persicae	plants
Wheat	Barley yellow dwarf	*Rhopalosiphum padi*	Late sowing (winter)
		Macrosiphum miscanthi	Systemic aphicides
Carrots	Carrot motley dwarf	Cavariella aegopodii	Late sowing (summer)
Potatoes	Potato Y	*Myzus persicae*	Resistant varieties
	Potato leaf roll	Aulacorthum solani	Late planting (summer)
		Macrosiphum euphorbiae	Systemic granules for early planting
Peas	Subterranean clover red leaf	*Aulacorthum solani*	
		Myzus persicae	Resistant varieties
	Pea leaf roll	Macrosiphum euphorbiae	
	Pea mosaic		

** Terminology after Martyn (1968)   * Most important vector

REFERENCES

Anon., 1961. A note on aphid resistant rape. *N.Z. Jl. Agric.* 102: 485.

Blackmore, L. W. 1967. Control of aphids in wheat. *Proc. 20th N.Z. Weed & Pest Control Conf.,* 236-46.

Close, R. C. 1967. The vectors of plant viruses. *Proc. 20th N.Z. Weed & Pest Control Conf.,* 197-203.

Close, R. C. and Lamb, K. P. 1961. Trapping study of some winged aphid vectors of plant virus diseases in Canterbury, New Zealand. *N.Z. Jl. agric. Res.* 4: 606-18.

Cognetti, G. 1961. Endomeiosis in parthenogenetic lines of aphids. *Experientia* 17: 168-9.

Cottier, W. 1953. The aphids of New Zealand. *Bull. N.Z. Dept. Scient. ind. Res.* 106: 383 pp.

Cottier, W. 1964. Insects of Campbell Island. Hemiptera. Homoptera: Aphididae. *Pacif. Ins. Mono.* 7: 236-7.

Dixon, A. F. G. 1971. The life-cycle and host preference of the bird cherry-oat aphid, *Rhopalosiphum padi* L., and their bearing on the theories of host alternation in aphids. *Ann. appl. Biol.* 68: 135-47.

Driver, C. M. 1966. Plant breeding in agricultural research. *N.Z. agric. Sci.* 1 (7): 13-6.

Eastop, V. F. 1966. A taxonomic study of Australian Aphidoidea (Homoptera). *Aust. Jl. Zool.* 14: 399-592.

Johnston, C. G. 1962. Aphid migration. *New Scient.* 15: 622-5.

———— 1967. International dispersal of insects and insect-borne viruses. *Neth. J. Pl. Path.* 73: Suppl. 1, 21-43.

Lees, A. D. 1966. The control of polymorphism in aphids. *Adv. Insect Physiol.* 3: 207-77.

Lamb, K. P. and Lowe, A. D. 1961. Studies of the ecology of the cabbage aphid: I introduction and population study, 1958-59. *N.Z. Jl. agric. Res.* 4: 619-42.

———— 1967. II Population study, 1959-60. *N.Z. Jl. agric. Res.* 10: 87-108.

Lowe, A. D. 1967. Sowing date as an aphid-virus control technique. *Proc. 20th N.Z. Weed & Pest Control Conf.,* 214-6.

———— 1968a. Alate aphids trapped over eight years at two sites in Canterbury, New Zealand. *N.Z. Jl. agric. Res.* 11: 829-48.

———— 1968b. The incidence of parasitism and disease in some populations of the cabbage aphid in New Zealand. *N.Z. Jl. agric. Res.* 11: 821-8.

———— 1969. A preliminary account of *Macrosiphum miscanthi* Takahashi on grasses and cereals in New Zealand. *N.Z. Ent.* 4 (2): 33-5.

———— 1971: Avoiding damage by aphids in carrot crops. *N.Z. Ent.* 5 (1): 49-51.

Martyn, E. B. 1968. Plant virus names. *Commonw. Mycol. Inst.,* England. 204 pp.

Palmer, T. P. and Smith, H. C. 1967. Aphid and virus resistance in crops. *Proc. 20th N.Z. Weed & Pest Control Conf.,* 208-13.

Rough, B. F. A. and Close, R. C. 1965. Use of disulfoton on potatoes. *Proc. 18th N.Z. Weed & Pest Control Conf.,* 188-96.

Sanderson, F R. and Mulholland, R. I. 1969. Effect of the grain aphid on yield and quality of wheat. *Proc. 20th N.Z. Weed and Pest Control Conf., 227-35.*

Smith, H. C., 1963. Spraying for control of yellow dwarf virus in wheat. *Proc. 13th Linc. Coll. Farmers' Conf.,* 102-9.

Smith, H. C., Giesen, H. J., and Allen, J. D. 1960. Control of motley dwarf virus disease in carrots. *N.Z. Comml. Grow.* 16 (2): 13-4.

Smith, H. C. 1968. Transmission of barley yellow dwarf virus in cereals by two aphid species. *N.Z. Jl. agric. Res.* 11: 500-5.

Wilson, J. and Close, R. C. 1973. Subterranean clover red leaf virus and other legume viruses in Canterbury. *N.Z. Jl. agric. Res.* (in press).

Valentine, E. W. 1967. Biological control of aphids. *Proc. 20th N.Z. Weed & Pest Control Conf.,* 204-7.

19

HOST SELECTION AND HOST SUITABILITY
IN *Aphidius smithi*
(Hymenoptera: Aphidiidae)

BY MANFRED MACKAUER

Department of Biological Sciences, Simon Fraser University, Burnaby, British Columbia, Canada

INTRODUCTION

The mechanisms that lead to host specificity in the entomophagous Hymenoptera include four distinct processes which have been described as host habitat finding, host finding, host acceptance, and host suitability (Doutt 1959; Salt 1935, 1938). The first three processes combined result in the selection of a host insect by the consecutive elimination of other species on ecological and behavioural grounds. As a rule host acceptance or otherwise depends on the actions of the adult female parasitoid which is free-living. Only the immature stages are parasitic. Most larvae are endoparasitic feeding on haemolymph and living host tissues; some larvae develop externally on the host. The parasitic stages of the entomophagous Hymenoptera generally are not involved in the decision processes which specify host choice. As a result, they have no influence on the selection of the medium (i.e., the host) which they exploit for development and growth. Approaches towards parasitic behaviour in the adult stage, phoresy, and larval host selection occur among some groups of Hymenoptera (Clausen 1940).

In the following sections I shall attempt to relate host selection by the aphid parasitoid *Aphidius smithi* (Hymenoptera: Aphidiidae) to host suitability. In particular, I will discuss whether adult female behaviour leads to the selection of hosts that provide optimal conditions for the development of the immature stages. Furthermore, I will argue that there is an evolutionary advantage to selection being imprecise. And I will attempt to show some of the implications with regard to biological control that follow from a consideration of host specificity as a dynamic concept.

Most of the data presented refer to the relationship between the parasitoid *A. smithi* and its main host, the pea aphid *(Acyrthosiphon pisum)*. The system was chosen for two reasons: First, extensive background information is available on both parasitoid and host; and second, the species can be easily maintained under laboratory conditions.

(1) HOST SELECTION IN *APHIDIUS SMITHI*

"Host specificity" refers to the restriction of a parasitoid to one or more host species which constitute the host range. Host specificity implies two things. One is that the parasitoid has certain requirements that can be satisfied only by some species (i.e, the hosts) and not by others; and two, that the parasitoid is able to exercise a choice in selecting appropriately suitable hosts. Host specificity does not imply that all species which potentially meet a parasitoid's (metabolic) requirements will be attacked in nature or, if attacked, will be equally susceptible. Moreover, not all developmental stages of a particular host may be suitable to a like degree or at all times. In fact, attributes such as host size, age, sex, or diet may have a modifying effect on the host-parasitoid relationship (e.g., Arthur & Wylie 1959; Clausen 1939; Gerling & Bar 1971; Salt 1941; Wilbert 1965 a, b; Wylie 1967).

While technically not strictly correct, it is convenient to distinguish between (a) host range selection, i.e., processes that lead to the acceptance or rejection of an insect *species* as a host, and (b) host instar selection, i.e., processes that result in discrimination between different developmental *stages* of an acceptable host species.

(a) The host range

Aphidius smithi has been reported in the literature as a parasitoid of the pea aphid (Mackauer & Stary 1967); no other aphids are known to be attacked under natural conditions.

Attempts to rear the parasitoid on alien hosts in the laboratory were only partly successful. Fox, Thurston & Pass (1967) were able to transfer *A. smithi* from the pea aphid to the green peach aphid (*Myzus persicae*); however, the parasitoid oviposited only into those green peach aphids that were feeding on broad bean but not into those on burley tobacco. Although *A. smithi* completed its development in the alien host, the period from oviposition to the emergence of the next generation lasted approximately 12 days at 21°C when reared on adult green peach aphids as compared with only 9-9.5 days on adult pea aphids (Fox, Pass & Thurston 1967). Other aphids that were accepted by the parasitoid for oviposition in the laboratory include *Macrosiphum (Sitobion) avenae* on oats (*Avena sativa*), *Megoura viciae* on broad bean (*Vicia faba*), *Microlophium evansi* on nettle (*Urtica dioica*), and *Acryrthosiphon pisum spartii* on broom (*Sarothamnus scoparius*), of which only the last species proved to be suitable as a host (Stary 1971). In addition, *A. smithi* attacked and occasionally oviposited into the rose aphid (*Macrosiphum rosae*) (Thomas, pers. comm.). Oviposition was not observed when *Dactynotus cichorii* (Stary 1971) or the cabbage aphid *(Brevicoryne brassicae)* were offered (Table I).

TABLE I

Host relationship of the parasitoid *Aphidius smithi* (Hymenoptera: Aphidiidae) under laboratory conditions (see text for details).

Host species	Acceptable[1]	Suitable[2]
HOMOPTERA: Aphididae		
Acyrthosiphon pisum	+	+
Acyrthosiphon pisum spartii	+	+
Brevicoryne brassicae	−	−
Dactynotus cichorii	−	−
Macrosiphum rosae	(+)	−
Macrosiphum (Sitobion) avenae	+	−
Megoura viciae	+	−
Microlophium evansi	+	−
Myzus persicae	+	(+)

[1] "Acceptable" refers to the potential host being accepted by a parasitoid female as indicated by attack (and oviposition).

[2] "Suitable" refers to the potential host permitting the successful growth and development of the immature parasitoid.

21

These records indicate that *A. smithi* has a relatively narrow host range which includes the pea aphid as the main host. Mackauer & Finlayson (1967), however, considered a strictly monophagous behaviour as unlikely. In view of the known host range of the closely related parasitoid *A. ervi* they suggested that, instead, the potential host range of *A. smithi* may be restricted to *Acyrthosiphon* species on Papilionaceae. Other aphids, such as the green peach aphid, apparently satisfy the nutritional requirements of the immature parasitoid. But it is unlikely that these species will be attacked in nature, except under conditions of stress.

(b) Discrimination between host instars

The oviposition response by *A. smithi* to different instars of the pea aphid was investigated first by Wiackowski (1962). He found that the second and third nymphal instars were selected over the first and fourth instars and adults (Table II). Other investigators (Fox, Pass & Thurston 1967) noted a strong preference by the parasitoid for the early first instar when instars were offered separately, one at a time. Parasitoid preference decreased with increasing host age. Young reproductive adults were as attractive as the third nymphal instar but post-reproductive adults were not attacked (Table II). When combinations of more than one aphid instar were offered, females did not exhibit a clear choice.

TABLE II

Relative preference of *Aphidius smithi* females for different developmental stages of the pea aphid, *Acyrthosiphon pisum*.

Host instar	Relative per cent of parasitism	
	Wiackowski (1962)	Fox *et al.* (1967)
Nymph$_1$ (early)	—	82
Nymph$_1$ (middle)	26.9	60
Nymph$_2$	47.9	—
Nymph$_3$	47.5	39
Nymph$_4$	9.4	—
Adult	8.0	33

Our own work with the parasitoid indicated that the results of such preference tests are influenced to a considerable degree by the experimental conditions. We used in our study 2- to 3-day old mated females. Each experimental series comprised 20 parasitoid females that were tested individually in their response to the following 7 age "test" groups: 0-4 hr old, 24, 48, 72, 96, 144 and 192 (± 3) hr old pea aphids. During the 3 hr test period each parasitoid female was provided with a total of 60 aphids: 30 marked 48-hr old, second instars (used as a "standard") and 30 "test" aphids.

Aphids were caged on broad bean plants maintained in a controlled environment chamber at 20 ± 1° C, 50-55% R.H., and a diel cycle of 16L/8D hrs.

Four criteria were considered for evaluating instar preference. (1) The total number of eggs laid per parasitoid female was determined by host dissection (Table 3): Females laid an average of 39 eggs during the 3 hr test period. They did not discriminate between "standard" aphids and aphids that were between 48 and 192 hr old; however, they laid significantly fewer eggs into 0-4 hr and 24-hr-old than

22

TABLE III

Number of eggs laid by *Aphidius smithi* females relative to host age. (Means of 20 females provided each with 30 48-hr. old "standard" and 30 "test" pea aphids, *Acyrthosiphon pisum*, for a 3 hr. test period).

Age (in hr)	Test host & Instar	Parasitoid Mean number of eggs laid[1]		
		Total	Standard	Test
0-4	N_1	40.50	23.25	17.25*
24	N_1	49.95	31.95	18.00**
48	N_2	27.60	14.25	13.35
72	N_2	31.80	16.05	15.75
96	N_3	50.25	23.70	26.55
144	N_4	33.75	17.10	16.65
192	Adult	40.05	19.80	20.25

[1] Difference between "standard" and "test" significant at the 5% (*) and 1% (**) level of probability.

TABLE IV

Number of eggs laid per host attacked by *Aphidius smithi* females relative to host age. (Means of 20 females provided each with 30 48-hr old "standard" and 30 "test" pea aphids. *Acyrthosiphon pisum*, for a 3 hr test period).

Age (in hr)	Test host & Instar	Parasitoid Mean number of eggs per host attacked[1]	
		Standard	Test
0-4	N_1	1.308	1.161
24	N_1	1.434	1.173**
48	N_2	1.040	1.106
72	N_2	1.122	1.236
96	N_3	1.414	1.329
144	N_4	1.200	1.146
192	Adult	1.320	1.386

[1] Difference between "standard" and "test" significant at the 5% (*) and 1% (**) level of probability.

into 48-hr-old "standard" hosts. (2) The mean number of eggs laid per host attacked, as determined by dissection, varied between 1.0 and 1.4 (Table IV). Females laid fewer eggs into 0-4 hr and 24-hr-old aphids than into "standard" nymphs offered at the same time. (3) The mean number of hosts attacked (Table V) can be determined in two ways. One way is by dissecting hosts after parasitoid attack. This value is indicative of the oviposition preference of the parasitoid female. A second way is by counting the number of "mummies" or of offspring produced in the next generation. This second value, when compared with the results of dissection, tells something about the suitability of the host (see Section 2). The overall rate of parasitism, as determined by dissection, was approximately 50%, with a mean of 52% of all "standard" aphids being parasitized. It is interesting to note that *A. smithi* females attacked equal numbers of "standard" and "test" aphids, except when offered a choice between 24- and 48-hr-old aphids. In the latter case they expressed a strong preference for the 48-hr-old "standard" nymphs. The difference between the 0-4 hr old and "standard" aphids almost reached statistical significance

23

TABLE V

Comparison between number of hosts parasitized by *Aphidius smithi* females and number of F_1 parasitoids emerging relative to host age. (Means of 20 females provided each with 30 48-hr old "standard" and 30 "test" pea aphids, *Acyrthosiphon pisum*, per 3 hr test period).

Test host		Parasitoid			
		Hosts parasitized vs. hosts yielding F_1 emergents (in per cent of total number of hosts available)[1]			
Age (in hr)	& Instar	Standard		Test	
		Parasitism	Emergence	Parasitism	Emergence
0-4	N_1	56.00	47.25*	48.50	39.75
24	N_1	73.00	41.75**	49.00	31.25**
48	N_2	45.00	44.00	40.00	39.80
72	N_2	45.00	44.25	40.50	37.75
96	N_3	54.50	49.75	59.00	44.75*
144	N_4	42.50	37.00	46.00	40.00
192	Adult	47.50	41.25	46.50	36.75**

[1] Difference between "parasitism" and "emergence" significant at the 5% (*) and 1% (**) level of probability.

at the 5% level. (4) The last criterion used was the sex ratio of the offspring produced on the various host groups. This was done on the assumption that females would deposit into the preferred host groups a relatively larger proportion of fertilized eggs, which develop into female offspring. The results indicated a secondary sex ratio which varied between 0.48 and 0.67 (= females as per cent of total number of offspring) with a mean of 0.54. There was no difference between "standard" and any of the "test" groups.

In summary, *A. smithi* females discriminate between first and second and older instars of the pea aphid. When given a choice, females attack first instar aphids with less frequency and lay fewer eggs into them than into older nymphal instars and pre-reproductive (viviparous) adults. Reproductive adults are distinguished from and are attacked less often than second (or third) instars. However, there is no good evidence of discrimination by the parasitoid between second, third, and fourth nympal instars. The secondary sex ratio of the offspring generation does not differ on different host instars. At present, it is not known whether this ratio correctly reflects the primary sex ratio, i.e., the ratio between fertilized and unfertilized eggs laid, or whether it is influenced by differential survival between male and female parasitoid larvae.

Experimental conditions that lead to superparasitism affect the oviposition behaviour of the parasitoid. In general, discrimination by *A. smithi* between different instars of the pea aphid decreases and the size of acceptable hosts appears to become a factor in host selection.

(2) HOST SUITABILITY

The term "host suitability" implies that the potential host provides a satisfactory environment for the successful growth and development of the immature parasitoid. It implies further that the host does not react immunologically to the presence of the parasitoid or, if it does react, that the parasitoid normally is able to overcome the host's defensive mechanisms.

Salt (1938) described a suitable host as one that can actually be parasitized by the adult and "on which the parasitoid can generally reproduce fertile offspring". A distinction between insusceptibility to attack and suitability for larval development is not trivial. In fact, the point is extremely important in arriving at a meaningful definition of host suitability. To be operationally useful, suitability must refer to a stage or process of parasitoid biology. Suitability, as defined here, is evidently not identical with Salt's concept. It refers only to the interactions between the host and the immature stages of the parasitoid, but excludes any interactions between the host and the adult parasitoid that may prevent attack or oviposition by physical, chemical, or behavioural defences.

Suitability is, in principle, measurable. In practice, however, the exact measurement is extremely difficult. The main handicap is that suitability is determined by a number of diverse and interacting properties of both host and parasitoid. Because very little is known about the causal relationships between these properties, available investigative methods are reduced to measuring host effects on certain attributes of the parasitoid. While this approach is not completely satisfactory, it produces results that can be interpreted in terms of host suitability.

We used three criteria to assess the suitability of different instars of the pea aphid for the development of *A. smithi*. (1) A comparison between the relative number of hosts attacked by the adult, as determined through dissection, and the number of hosts actually producing parasitoids is given in Table V. There was a highly significant difference between these values in the 192-hr-old "test" group indicating that the per cent of F_1 parasitoids produced on pre-reproductive adult aphids was less than expected on the basis of oviposition frequency. A difference of a similar magnitude in the 24-hr-old "test" group was paralleled in the "standard" group reared on the same host plant suggesting that aphid survival in general was poor in that instance. (2) Thomas (unpublished) determined the number and growth of teratocytes which the parasitoid produced in different aphid instars. She found that the mean teratocyte number was inversely proportional to the age of the host at the beginning of parasitism, cell numbers decreasing from a mean of 30 to 25 in instars I to IV, respectively. These numbers did not change significantly until the beginning of cell lysis during the last phase of larval development. Teratocyte growth during the post-eclosion phase differed at the 5% level of significance, the greatest growth rate being achieved in second instars followed by the third, fourth and first instars. The total teratocyte burden (i.e., the product of teratocyte number times volume) was greatest in second instar aphids followed by first, third and fourth instars in that order. These data were interpreted as evidence of age resistance in older hosts. (3) Another useful criterion of host suitability is the relative increase in dry weight of parasitoid larvae. Smith (unpublished) found that *A. smithi* larvae reached a dry weight of approximately 0.4 mg after 6 days, if oviposition took place in 48-hr-old, second instar nymphs, while other larvae required 7 days to reach a comparable weight on older nymphs (Table VI). The maximum dry weight at pupation of parasitoids that developed from eggs laid in 12-hr-old, first instars was little more than one half the weight gained on older hosts (Table VII). (4) Also relevant are observations by Fox & Thurston (1967) who reported that the average pre-imaginal developmental period was correlated with host size. Development required an average of 10.5 days at 21° C

TABLE VI

Dry weight of 6-day old larvae of *Aphidius smithi* developing in different instars of the pea aphid, *Acyrthosiphon pisum*, at 20°C., 50-55% R.H., and 16L/8D hr. diel.

Age at parasitization (in hr)	Host & Instar	n	Parasitoid Dry weight (Mean ± S.E.) (in 1 x 10^{-3} mg)
12	N_1	15	96.5 ± 7.7
48	N_2	10	403.6 ± 18.4
84	N_3	13	197.4 ± 12.0
144	N_4	9	194.9 ± 21.0

TABLE VII

Dry weight at pupation of *Aphidius smithi* developing in different nymphal instars of the pea aphid, *Acyrthosiphon pisum*, at 20°C., 50-55% R.H., and 16 L/8D hr. diel.

Age at parasitization (in hr)	Host & Instar	n	Days after parasitization	Parasitoid Dry weight (Mean ± S.E.) (in 1 x 10^{-3} mg)
12	N_1	12	8	203.4 ± 6.7
48	N_2	10	6	403.6 ± 18.4
84	N_3	8	7	391.1 ± 49.1
144	N_4	11	8	351.0 ± 16.5

in the small first instar nymphs and decreased progressively on older and larger aphids, with only 9-9.5 days required on adult pea aphids.

(3) CONCLUSIONS

In the previous section I have attempted to show two things. First, I have shown that mated females of the aphid parasitoid *A. smithi* select for oviposition second, third and fourth instars of the pea aphid in preference to first instars and reproductive viviparous adults. Second, on the condition that growth and survival are meaningful indicators of host optimality,[1] I have shown that second instar pea aphids are more suitable for the development of the immature parasitoid stages than first, third and fourth instars.

Evidently, these data are incomplete and do not assure a proper understanding of all aspects of host selection and host suitability. However, the results are sufficiently consistent to enable an interpretation in a more general way . The first question which I shall consider concerns the host range. In particular, I shall examine the relationship between the "host acceptability range" of the parasitoid female and the "host suitability range" of the parasitoid larva. Evidence summarized in Table 1 clearly indicates that even such relatively specific parasitoids as *A. smithi* readily attack alien hosts if deprived of a more suitable choice. Moreover, an aphid's lack of suitability does not prevent oviposition. Analysis of the relationship between *A. smithi* and its usual host, the pea aphid, confirms that the parasitoid

[1] In the sense used here, the "optimal" host is one on which the parasitoid's innate capacity of increase is maximized.

female is more tolerant of differences, if any, between available host instars than optimality for larval development would suggest. The only restriction seems to be that females do not readily oviposit into marginally suitable hosts, except under conditions of stress.

The potential production of offspring is determined by the degree of correlation between host selection and host suitability. Production is maximized if selection by the female leads to oviposition into hosts that are optimally suitable for the development of the immature stages. If females make the wrong choice too many times, there is a chance that the species will become extinct. We would expect, therefore, that parasitoid females act in a highly efficient manner in selecting appropriately suitable hosts. Salt (1938) in fact suggested that host selection plays a greater role in defining the host range of the entomophagous Hymenoptera than suitability. For this reason it is surprising that in nature, as well as in the laboratory, females oviposit with relative frequency into unsuitable hosts (Griffiths 1960; Miller 1929; Sekhar 1960; Wilbert 1964). The majority of such cases, probably occurring under conditions of stress, can be classified as "failures" of the sensory system. Stress, however, is not a satisfactory general explanation for the absence of discrimination between differently suitable instars of the same host species (Sections 1b and 2). More satisfactory are perhaps the following arguments which consider errors of optimal host selection in the context of persistence (Thoday 1953).

In groups such as the parasitic Hymenoptera, a division of function is suggested between adult and immature stages. Adult females presumably are adapted to host selection, while the immature stages are adapted to host exploitation. As already stated, a high degree of adaptedness in both functions would ensure maximum fecundity; however, it would not necessarily ensure the survival of the population over a long period of time. Slobodkin (1968) suggested that the best evolutionary strategy for persistence of a species living in a changeable environment is to maximize its homeostatic ability "so as to avoid or counteract the effects of introduced variance" without undergoing any genetic change. Excepting catastrophic events, it would appear that the greatest danger to a parasitoid's persistence arises from phenotypic changes of the host, in particular from those changes that may interfere with the host recognition system. The probability of extinction as a consequence of such changes can be reduced, if the standard of host acceptance is relaxed to less than absolute. The immediate cost would be a reduction in the parasitoid's reproductive achievement which, however, may be tolerable considering the high number of eggs available to species such as *A. smithi* (Mackauer 1971).

Flexibility in host selection provides an additional advantage insofar as it ensures that species or strains that (in the course of their evolution) become suitable as hosts will be explored, thus permitting secondary extensions of the host range.

These arguments in no way deny that selection leading to adaptation (Pimentel 1968; Pimentel & Stone 1968) contribute to a parasitoid's ability to maintain itself on a particular host or host complex. Selection operating through gene frequency changes in the population may be a necessary, yet not always a desirable response to sudden but minor perturbations. By dividing host specificity into two stage-separated components and by relaxing the criteria of host selection but not those of host exploitation, the entomophagous Hymenoptera have evolved an effective strategy for persistence, i.e., to avoid response to minor host changes by retaining a tolerable degree of flexibility.

27

My next and final point is concerned with biological control. Introduced parasitoids frequently are remarkably successful in keeping a pest at low densities. Pimentel (1963, 1968) predicted from the results of laboratory tests that a long association between host and parasitoid eventually should lead to a mutualistic relationship operating through a genetic feed-back system. Yet, there is no good evidence that, in nature, these parasitoids have lost their effectiveness as regulatory agents with time, or that their hosts developed resistance to them. How can we account for this apparent paradox? Huffaker, Messenger & DeBach (1971) rejected the predicted consequences of "co-evolution" in the main on two grounds. One, a genetic feed-back mechanism does not constitute a regulatory process which automatically must lead to homeostasis; and two, the interaction between insect host and parasitoid is lethal resulting in the death of one or the other. I shall concern myself only with their second point.

Insects, apparently, have not developed any tolerance to parasitoids at the individual level. Huffaker *et al.* suggested as an explanation that highly specific parasitoids remained effective because they were able to meet the "evolutionary challenge" of resistance while, by implication, other less specific parasitoids were unable to do so. It is evident that insect parasitoids, whether effective biological control agents or not, must have escaped the defense reactions of their hosts to have survived. It is arguable and would be difficult to prove, however, that they maintained effective control and without change "by countering trends towards such (host) resistance".

Such tenuous assumptions in fact may not be necessary to explain the continuing high performance of these natural enemies. The apparent stability, I submit, could be the result of these parasitoids not being "locked" to a narrowly defined and changeable host condition rather than because of a narrow specialization.

Acknowledgment

Part of the work discussed here was supported by a grant from the National Research Council of Canada.

REFERENCES

Arthur, A. P. and Wylie, H. G. 1959. Effects of host size on sex ratio, development time and size of *Pimpla turionellae* (Hym. Ichneumonidae). *Entomophaga*, 4, 297-301.

Clausen, C. P. 1939. The effects of host size upon the sex ratio of hymenopterous parasites and its relation to methods of rearing and colonization. *J. N. Y. ent. Soc.*, 47, 1-9.

———— 1940. *Entomophagous Insects*. McGraw-Hill, New York.

Doutt, R. L. 1959. The biology of parasitic Hymenoptera. *A. Rev. Ent.*, 4, 161-182.

Fox, P. M., Pass, B. C. and Thurston, R. 1967. Laboratory studies on the rearing of *Aphidius smithi* (Hymenoptera: Braconidae) and its parasitism of *Acyrthosiphon pisum* (Homoptera: Aphididae). *Ann. ent. Soc. Am.*, 60, 1083-1087.

Fox, P. M., Thurston, R. and Pass, B. C. 1967. Notes on *Myzus persicae* (Homoptera: Aphididae) as a host for *Aphidius smithi* (Hymenoptera: Braconidae). *Ann. ent. Soc. Am.*, 60, 708-709.

Gerling, D. and Bar, D. 1971. Reciprocal host-parasite relations as exemplified by *Chrysomphalus aonidum* (Homoptera: Diaspididae) and *Pteropterix smithi* (Hymenoptera: Aphelinidae). *Entomophaga*, 16, 37-44.

Griffiths, D. C. 1960. The behaviour and specificity of *Monoctonus paludum* Marshall (Hym., Braconidae), a parasite of *Nasonovia ribis-nigri* (Mosley) on lettuce. *Bull. ent. Res.*, 51, 303-319.

Huffaker, C. B., Messenger, P. S. and DeBach, P. 1971. The natural enemy component in natural control and the theory of biological control. *In:* Huffaker, C. B. (ed.), *Biological Control,* pp. 16-67. Plenum Press, New York and London.

Mackauer, M. 1971. *Acyrthosiphon pisum* (Harris), pea aphid (Homoptera: Aphididae). *In: Biological Control Programmes against Insects and Weeds in Canada 1959-1968,* pp. 3-10. Tech. Commun. Commonw. Inst. biol. Control, 4.

Mackauer, M. and Finlayson, T. 1967. The hymenopterous parasites (Hymenoptera: Aphidiidae et Aphelinidae) of the pea aphid in eastern North America. *Can. Ent.,* 99, 1051-1082.

Mackauer, M. and Stary, P. 1967. World Aphidiidae (Hym. Ichneumonoidea). *In: Index of Entomophagous Insects.* Le François, Paris.

Miller, R. L. 1929. A contribution to the biology and control of the green citrus aphid, *Aphis spiraecola* Patch. *Tech. Bull. Fla agric. Exp. Stn,* 203, 431-476.

Pimentel, D. 1963. Introducing parasites and predators to control native pests. *Can. Ent.,* 95, 785-792.

———— 1968. Population regulation and genetic feed-back. *Science,* 159, 1432-1437.

Pimentel, D. and Stone, F. A. 1968. Evolution and population ecology of parasite-host systems. *Can. Ent.,* 100, 655-662.

Salt, G. 1935. Experimental studies in insect parasitism. III. Host selection. *Proc. R. Soc. Lond. (B),* 117, 413-435.

———— 1938. Experimental studies in insect parasitism. VI. Host suitability. *Bull. ent. Res.,* 29, 223-246.

———— 1941. The effects of hosts upon their insect parasites. *Biol. Rev.,* 16, 239-264.

Sekhar, P. S. 1960. Host relationships of *Aphidius testaceipes* (Cresson) and *Praon aguti* (Smith), primary parasites of aphids. *Can. J. Zool.,* 38, 593-603.

Slobodkin, L. B. 1968. Toward a predictive theory of evolution. *In:* Lewontin, R. C. (ed.), *Population Biology and Evolution,* pp. 187-205. Syracuse Univ. Press.

Stary, P. 1971. Alternative hosts of *Aphidius smithi,* an introduced parasite of the pea aphid in central Europe (Hom. Aphididae; Hym. Aphidiidae). *Ann. ent. Soc. Fr., N. S.,* 7, 351-355.

Thoday, J. M. 1953. Components of fitness. *Symp. Soc. Exp. Biol.,* 7, 96-113.

Wiackowski, S. K. 1962. Studies on the biology and ecology of *Aphidius smithi* Sharma and Subba Rao (Hymenoptera: Braconidae), a parasite of the pea aphid. *Acyrthosiphon pisum* (Harr.) (Homoptera, Aphididae). *Polskie Pismo ent.,* 32, 253-310.

Wilbert, H. 1964. Das Ausleseverhalten von *Aphelinus semiflavus* Howard und die Abwehrreaktionen seiner Wirte. *Beitr. Ent.,* 14, 159-219.

———— 1965 a. Die Grössenvariablltät von *Aphelinus semiflavus* Howard (Hym: Aphelinidae) und ihre Ursachen. *Z. Pfl. Krankh.,* 72, 670-684.

———— 1965 b. Die Auswirkungen der Kärpergrösse von *Aphelinus semiflavus* Howard (Hym.: Aphelinidae) auf einige Organe und ihre Leistungsfähigkeit. *Z. Morph. Ökol. Tiere,* 55, 804-834.

Wylie, H. G. 1967. Some effects of host size on *Nasonia vitripennis* and *Muscidifurax raptor* (Hymenoptera: Pteromalidae). *Can. Ent.,* 99, 742-748.

PATHOGENS OF APHIDS

By Irvin M. Hall

Division of Biological Control, University of California, Riverside, California

The recent survey by Gustafsson (1971) on microbial control of aphids has reiterated the fact long known to those who have studied diseases of these insects that pathogens of aphids are largely limited to certain groups of entomogenous fungi, and the paucity of information on the susceptibility of aphids to any other type of microorganism would suggest that activity against aphids by pathogens other than fungi would at best be of limited scope in the overall suppression of aphid populations.

Gustafsson (1971) mentions that pathogenic bacteria occur rarely in aphids, and the only case that he cites is that of a bacteriosis in *Therioaphis trifolii* (Monell) diagnosed by Steinhaus & Marsh (1962). This diagnostic report states only that the bacteria present were miscellaneous small gram-negative rods. It is most probable that they were accidental outgrowths of normal intestinal flora rather than primary pathogens. In the course of our own investigations, the diagnoses of a few dead, diseased *Acyrthosiphon pisum* (Harris) discovered on foliage collected from a lucerne field previously sprayed with a commercial preparation of *Bacillus thuringiensis* var. *thuringiensis* Berliner for control of a weevil infestation revealed that the aphids had died of a septicemia and the body fluids were filled with large numbers of cells of the crystalliferous bacillus. This find would indicate that *A. pisum* does possess a susceptibility of sorts to *B. thuringiensis* var. *thuringiensis*. However, the piercing and sucking mode of feeding by the aphid would preclude more than chance ingestion of spores or associated toxins in quantities sufficient to induce infection, thereby making the bacillus at best only a fortuitous pathogen, of little consequence in the microbial suppression of the pest.

The absence of viral pathogens of aphids also is indicated by Gustafsson (1971) who states that virus infections have not been definitely demonstrated in any species of the group. Virus-like particles, both intra- and extracellular, have been described by Moericke (1963), Lee (7965) and Parrish & Briggs (1966) from several viruliferous and nonviruliferous aphids. The first two workers reported their beliefs that the particles were unrelated to plant viruses vectored by the aphids under study, and the latter stated that the particles could represent latent infection of the aphid, a plant virus, or a normal component of the aphid cell, conditions which are doubted by Gustafsson, although he does not provide an explanation as to what the particles might be.

A number of species of hyphomycetous imperfect fungi (Deuteromycetes) have been reported to attack aphids. The fungi *Cephalosporium aphidicola* Petch, *C. muscarium* Petch, *Cladosporium aphidis* Thuem., *Hirsutella aphidis* Petch and *Paecilomyces (Spicaria) farinosus* (Dicks ex. Fr) Brown and Smith were recorded from aphid hosts by Petch (1932, 1948), and are mentioned in the subsequent listings of entomogenous fungi in Britain by Leatherdale (1958, 1970) and the most recent review by Gustafsson (1971). Since they have not been reported by other workers, it must be assumed that they occur rarely in nature and at best play a minimal role in the suppression of aphid populations which they are reported to attack.

The only imperfect fungus to be studied to any degree to determine its role in the biological control of aphid pests is *Acrostalagmus aphidum* Oud. Numerous field tests were conducted with this fungus in Puerto Rico against *Myzus persicae* (Sulzer) and *Aphis gossypii* Glover, on egg plant by Nolla (1929), who reported good control following spraying of infested plants with spore suspensions. However, Wolcott (1955), in his review of this work, stated that "even under . . . weather conditions approaching optimum, only a majority of the aphids were killed at any time, and in no case reported did the mortality approach totality". Wolcott's own results of studies conducted in the 1940's with *A. aphidum* against heavy infestations of *Sipha flava* (Forbes) on young sugarcane in Puerto Rico were much more impressive, inasmuch as he found that under equally optimum weather conditions of extended periods of rainfall or high humidity at tropical temperatures, application of infective stages of the fungus could bring about mass infection and total destruction of the pest population on the treated foliage.

The only other report on trials with *A. aphidum* is that of Shands *et al.* (1958), who claim successful infection of small numbers of *Macrosiphum euphorbiae* (Thomas) following application of spores of the fungus. Moreover, the collection of a few infected aphids in check plots adjacent to the areas treated led them to believe that some spread of the fungus had taken place. This claimed establishment and possible spread must be doubted, since during the 10-year study that followed, in which thousands of dead, diseased aphids of several species infesting potatoes in northeastern Maine were collected and examined, none was found to be infected by *A. aphidum* (Shands *et al.*, 1962; Shands *et al.*, 1963; Shands *et al.*, 1972). It is possible that the fungus requires tropical weather conditions for development .

Other aphid hosts of *A. aphidum* recorded from North American collections, according to Charles (1941) are *Macrosiphoniella sanborni* (Gillette), *Hyadaphis erysimi* (Kaltenbach), *Coloradoa rufomaculata* (Wilson) and *Toxoptera aurantii* (Fonscolombe).

The most important fungi causing diseases of aphids belong to the genus *Entomophthora (=Empusa)* of the family Entomophthoraceae within the small, but distinct, order Entomophthorales of the higher Phycomycetes. The members of this genus have in common certain structural characters, variations of which are used to identify each species. Their mycelium within the host body generally becomes much reduced, forming hyphal bodies of varied length and shape that pack the body cavity. Asexual reproduction is by means of conidial spores which are formed and shot off singly from the tips of branched or unbranched conidiophores. Sexual reproduction in some species is by the conjugation of hyphal bodies to form thick-walled zygospores, although in other species, morphologically similar resting spores, called azygospores, are formed without conjugation. Other structures formed by some, but not all, of the fungi are cystidia (sterile conidiophores) and rhizoids or hold-fasts.

Of the 100 or more species of *Entomophthora* listed by MacLeod (1963) 13 are recognized to attack aphids under natural conditions, and one species isolated from a different type of insect has been reported to be capable of infecting aphids under experimental conditions (Krejzova, 1972). The species of *Entomophthora* isolated from aphid hosts are presented below, along with their synonomy (as presented by Gustafsson (1965)), distinctive morphological characterization, and listing of major

31

aphid hosts as extracted from the cataloguing of Charles (1941), Gustafsson (1965), Leatherdale (1970), Petch (1948) and Thaxter (1888).

Entomophthora aphidis Hoffmann

Syn. *Tarichium aphidis* Cohn 1870; *Empusa aphidis* (Hoffman.) Thaxter 1888

Conidia: ovoid to elliptical to subfusiform; commonly asymmetrical and very variable; with papillate base and containing numerous oil globules; average size 25 x 12 μ, maximum 40 x 16 μ (Thaxter, 1888; variable by other authors); secondary conidia like the primary, or short ovoid with a single large oil globule. *Conidiophores:* branched, but often unbranched; color of coalesced conidiophores varies from white to yellowish or flesh color to a brick-red tint at time of death of host. *Hyphal Bodies:* according to Thaxter (1888), they are spherical, germinating in all directions. This claim is doubted, since MacLeod (1955), Grobler *et al.* (1962) and Gustafsson (1965) indicate that they are short, thick, sometimes branched fragments of hyphae, varying in shape and size. *Cystidia:* rather slender and tapering at their extremities. *Resting Spores:* spherical; thick walled; epispore roughened (patterned) and brown in color; 33-45 μ in diameter; and borne terminally or laterally on hyphae. Gustafsson (1965) states that they are zygospores. *Host Attachment:* rhizoids, few in number, and usually terminating in a disc-like expansion.

Entomophthora aphidis occurs on aphids of numerous genera in many parts of the world. Its partial host list includes: *Acyrthosiphon dirhodum* (Walker), *A. pisum* (Harris), *A solani* (Kaltenbach), *Aphis craccae* Linnaeus, *A. fabae* Scopoli, *A. forbesi* Weed, *A. nasturtii* Kaltenbach, *A. pomi* DeGeer, *A. rumicis* Linnaeus, *A. sambuci* Linnaeus, *Brachycaudus helichrysi* (Kaltenbach), *Brachycolus asparagi* Mordvilko, *Brevicoryne brassicae* (Linnaeus), *Capitophorus hippophaes* (Walker), *Cavariella pastinacae* (Linnaeus), *Macrosiphoniella tanacetaria* (Kaltenbach), *Macrosiphum euphorbiae* (Thomas), *M. rosae* (Linnaeus), *Microlophium evansi* (Theobald), *Myzus persicae* (Sulzer), *Nasonovia lactucae* (Linnaeus), *N. lampsanae* (Börner), *Pemphigus bursarius* (Linnaeus), *Rhopalomyzus lonicerae* (Siebold), *Rhopalosiphoninus staphyleae* (Koch), *Rhopalosiphum maidis* (Fitch), *R. padi* (Linnaeus), and *Schizolachnus piniradiatae* (Davidson).

Entomophthora atrosperma Petch 1932

Conidia, Conidiophores, Hyphal Bodies, and *Cystidia:* not described. *Resting Spores:* blackish-brown, globose; 38-45 μ in diameter; epispore with spines (2 μ in length). *Host Attachment:* a few hyaline hyphae.

The original description by Petch (1932) gives the most minimal information in which the host was an unidentified aphid collected in Grassington, England, on September 12, 1931, by F. A. Mason. The descriptive information ordinarily would be insufficient for use in diagnostic procedures, which could explain why it never has been observed since the original collection. However, as noted by MacLeod (1963), the distinctive epispore should make it recognizable when collected in the future.

Entomophthora coronata (Costantin) Kevorkian 1937

Syn. *Boudierella coronata* Costantin 1897; *Delacroixia coronata* Sacc. and Syd. (Saccardo 1899); *Conidiobolus villosus* Martin 1925

Conidia: rather large and globose, with a predominant basal papilla; average diameter (exclusive of papilla) 35-45 μ, with extremes of 12 to 56 μ noted by various workers (Gustafsson, 1965). Microconidia minute, reportedly pyriform or subglobose, forming on short stalks from the primary conidia. *Conidiophores:* mostly unbranched and erect. *Hyphal Bodies:* not mentioned in original description, but reported subsequently by Schaefer (1941) to be ramified fragments of varied length of hyphae which are about 12 μ in diameter. *Cystidia: absent.* *Resting Spores:* reported to be similar to the conidia, but with long hair-like appendages, thereby called by some workers "villose conidia". (This author questions that these are true resting spores, since in one culture of *E. coronata* in a temperature study conducted more than 15 years ago, typical spherical, thick-walled resting spores were noted. This never has been reported because repeated efforts to produce additional spores under similar and varied conditions failed). *Host Attachment:* rhizoids are absent; attachment if any must be by means of the insertion of the proboscis.

Natural hosts of *E. coronata* include: *Acyrthosiphon solani* (Kaltenbach), *Aphis fabae* Scopoli, *A. nasturtii* Kaltenbach, *Brevicoryne brassicae* (Linnaeus), *Macrosiphum euphorbiae* (Thomas), *Megoura viciae* Buckton, *Myzus persicae* (Sulzer), and *Therioaphis maculata* (Buckton).

Entomophthora exitialis Hall and Dunn 1957

Conidia: ovoid with rounded ends, occasionally pyriform to irregular and, although smaller in size, greatly resemble the conidia of *E. aphidis;* size 16-23 μ x 9-12 μ, average 18-20 x 11 μ. Secondary conidia similar, but smaller and formed at the tips of short germ tubes growing terminally or laterally from primary conidia. *Conidiophores:* branched, short, form a reddish cover over the entire host body. *Hyphal Bodies:* short, slender sections of hyphae with tapered ends; some irregular in shape; 8-11 μ in diameter, 23-30 μ in length. *Cystidia:* rare to absent on host. *Resting Spores:* reported in original description to be azygospores, spherical, thick-walled, with smooth epispore, measuring 24-32 μ in diameter, average 27 μ (Gustafsson (1965) reports slightly larger measurements of 23-29 μ, average 30 μ). *Host Attachment:* rhizoids.

This fungus originally was considered to be specific to *Therioaphis maculata* ((Buckton), and it was found to occur throughout the world where the host occurs. More recently, it was found on *Aphis fabae* Scopoli by Gustafsson (1965).

Entomophthora fresenii (Nowakowski) Gustafsson 1965

Sny. *Empusa fresenii* Nowakowski 1883; *Neozygites aphidis* Witlaczil 1885; *Empusa (Triplosporium) fresenii* (Nowakowski) Thaxter 1888

Conidia: reported to be nearly spherical to short ovoid, often with a short, truncate or papillate base, with granular contents and slightly smoky in color; measuring from 18 x 15 μ to 20 x 18 μ (Gustafsson (1965) reports slightly larger measurements from his and other work of 16-27 μ long x 13-24 μ wide, averaging 22-24 μ x 17-20 μ). The secondary conidia are like the primary or almond shaped and darker. *Conidiophores:* unbranched. *Hyphal Bodies:* reported to be small, spherical. *Cystidia:* absent. *Resting Spores:* reported by Soper and MacLeod (1963) to be broadly elliptical or subovoid; with smooth epispore; black in color; zygospores: 24-42 μ long x 16-30 μ wide, averaging 30.5 x 22 μ. *Host Attachment:* rhizoids absent; attachment if any by means of insertion of the proboscis.

Natural hosts for *E. fresenii* include: *Acyrthosiphon pisum* (Harris), *Aphis craccae* Linnaeus, *A. fabae* Scopoli, *A. pomi* DeGeer, *Dactynotus taraxaci* (Kaltenbach), *Myzus persicae* (Sulzer), *Rhopalosiphum fitchii* (Sanderson), and *Schizolachnus piniradiatae* (Davidson).

Entomophthora lageniformis (Thaxter) 1888

Syn. *Empusa (Triplosporium) lageniformis* Thaxter 1888

Conidia: flask-shaped with a truncate, hardly papillate, base, rounded apex and evenly granular contents; slightly smoky color; measurements average 35 x 20 μ, maximum 38 x 30 μ. Secondary conidia like the primary, or almond-shaped and borne obliquely on capillary conidiophores. *Conidiophores:* unbranched, or when young sometimes fasciculate or pseudodigitate. *Hyphal Bodies:* not mentioned in the original description and, therefore, not known. *Cystidia:* absent. *Resting Spores:* unknown. *Host Attachment:* rhizoids absent; attachment by insertion of the proboscis.

Information on hosts is extremely vague, since Thaxter (1888) and subsequent references state only that the fungus was found on aphids infesting *Betula populifolia* in Maine, Massachusetts and North Carolina of eastern North America. Thaxter stated also that the species is quite similar to *E. fresenii,* but with larger dimensions.

Entomophthora obscura Hall and Dunn 1957

Conidia: spherical or globose, with papillate base; contents quite granular; only a few formed on the surface of the host; measurements 32-44 μ in diameter (exclusive of the papilla), average 40 μ. Secondary conidia like the primary, but smaller. *Conidiophores:* unbranched, with only a few extending through the host integument. *Hyphal Bodies:* short sections of hyphae, with rounded ends; sometimes curved, twisted or branched; 15-23 μ in diameter, 50-200 μ in length. *Resting Spores:* generally spherical, but some irregular forms; thick walled; epispore smooth; dense granular cytoplasm, often with one to several large vacuoles or oil globules; azygospores common, but some zygospores noted; 35-55 μ in diameter *Host Attachment:* rhizoids absent; attachment by insertion of the proboscis.

The only host from which *E. obscura* has been positively identified is *Therioaphis maculata* Buckton. Very recently, a fungus that appeared to be very near to *E. obscura* was diagnosed by the author from *Acyrthosiphon pisum* (Harris) from Argentina.

Entomophthora occidentalis (Thaxter) 1888

Syn. *Empusa occidentalis* Thaxter 1888

Conidia: long-elliptical to cylindrical, sometimes slightly fusiform, often tapering strongly toward the apex; with a broad, rounded papillate base; measurements average 35 x 10 μ, maximum 45 x 12 μ; contents usually finely granular, sometimes with larger globules. Secondary conidia like the primary or long almond-shaped and borne obliquely on capillary conidiophores. *Conidiophores:* irregularly digitate, coalescing over the host in a white or slightly yellowish mass. *Hyphal Bodies:* not mentioned directly in original description, but probably short sections of hyphae. *Cystidia:* slender, slightly tapering. *Resting Spores:* spherical; thick-walled; epispore smooth; hyaline; 20-35 μ in diameter; azygospores (but possibly forming zygospores, also). *Host Attachment:* numerous rhizoids.

The only hosts listed by Thaxter were aphids on *Betula populifolia* in Maine and Massachusetts of northeastern United States. This could be the single species *Euceraphis betulae* (Linnaeus) which infests all kinds of birch trees in that area. Petch (1948) also lists *Drepanosiphum platanoidis* (Schrank) as a host in England.

Entomophthora planchoniana Cornu 1873

Syn. *Empusa planchoniana* Petch 1938 non Thaxter 1888: *Entomophthora ferruginea* Phillips 1886; *Entomophthora chromaphidis* Burger and Swain 1918.

Conidia: bell-shaped to globose, with broad truncate base, and furnished with an apical point; measurements 17-23 x 12-20 μ (Gustafsson (1965) reports slightly smaller dimensions with an average of 19 x 15 μ). Secondary conidia like the primary, but smaller; 15-20 x 12-14 μ; with or without an apical point; and produced by direct budding from the primary conidia. *Conidiophores:* unbranched; covering host in continuous even stratum or in irregular confluent masses, turning insect reddish in color. *Hyphal Bodies:* not described by Cornu or Petch (1937), but pictured by Gustafsson (1965) as elongated twisted sections of hyphae. *Cystidia:* absent. *Resting Spores:* described and illustrated by Gustafsson (1965) as spherical azygospores, formed terminally on hyphae; thick-walled at maturity, with a dark reddish-brown easily removed epispore; measurements varied from 25-36 μ in diameter, average 30 μ. *Host Attachment:* rhizoids consisting of thick bundles of hyphae (Gustafsson, 1965).

The list of hosts of this fungus includes: *Acyrthosiphon dirhodum* (Walker), *A. pisum* (Harris), *Aphis fabae* Scopoli, *A. gossypii* Glover, *A. ilicis* Kaltenbach, *A. sambuci* Linnaeus, *A. spiraecola* Patch, *Brachycaudus helichrysi* (Kaltenbach), *Cavariella aegopodii* (Scopoli), *C. pastinacae* (Linnaeus), *C. theobaldi* (Gillette and Bragg), *Chaetosiphon fragaefolii* (Cockerell), *Dysaphis plantaginea* (Passerini), *Liosomaphis berberidis* (Kaltenbach), *Macrosiphum euphorbiae* (Thomas), *M. rosae* (Linnaeus), *Microlophium evansi* (Theobald), *Myzus persicae* (Sulzer), *Nasonovia lactucae* (Linnaeus), and *Rhopalosiphum padi* (Linnaeus).

Enthomophthora pyriformis Thoizon 1967

Conidia: primary forms pyriform (this would conform with almost-spherical to subglobose with respect to terminology used in the descriptions of similarly shaped conidia of *E. coronata, E. obscura, E. thaxteriana,* and *E. virulenta*), with large and long basal papillae; measurements 12-25 μ in diameter (exclusive of papilla), average 19 μ. Secondary conidia smaller (18 μ) and variable in shape from pyriform to spherical. *Conidiophores:* not mentioned in the original description, but probably are unbranched because of the multinucleate condition of the conidia. *Hyphal Bodies:* short sections of hyphae more or less branched. *Cystidia:* absent. *Resting Spores:* spherical; assumed to be thick walled, although not mentioned in the original description; smooth epispore; hyaline; measurements 12-25 μ, average 17-21 μ. *Host Attachment:* rhizoids absent.

The natural host of this fungus is *Rhopalosiphum insertum* (Walker). Thoizon (1967) also reports the experimental infection of *Aphis fabae* Scopoli, *Macrosiphum avenae* (Fabricius), and *Rhopalosiphum padi* (Linnaeus).

Entomophthora sphaerosperma Fresenius 1856

Syn. *Tarichium sphaerospermum* Cohn 1875; *Empusa radicans* Brefeld 1870; *Entomophthora phytonomi* Arthur 1886; *Empusa sphaerosperma* (Fres.) Thaxter 1888.

Conidia: long-elliptical to nearly cylindrical, papillate at the base and tapering very slightly near the rounded apex; measurements according to Thaxter (1888) ranged between 15-26 x 5-8 μ, average 20 x 5.5 μ, with averages of other workers (Gustafsson, 1965) varying particularly in width up to 24 x 11 μ. Secondary conidia like the primary, or long almond-shaped and borne on capillary conidiophores. *Conidiophores:* branched, forming a covering over the surface of the host body. *Hyphal Bodies:* sections of hyphae, elongate or almost round. *Cystidia:* slender, tapering, not abundant. *Resting Spores:* spherical, thick-walled, smooth epispore, hyaline; 20-35 μ in diameter, average 25 μ ,according to Thaxter (1888) (variations from these measurements may be encountered since Gustafsson (1965) reports a range of 21-28 μ, average 23 μ, and this author has seen resting spores of *E. sphaerosperma* from a coleopterous host averaging nearly 50 μ in diameter). *Host Attachment:* numerous rhizoids.

E. sphaerosperma is considered to be one of the most common of *Entomophthora* species in the world, attacking insects from many orders. It is apparent that only a small number of aphid species are among its hosts, and these include *Acyrthosiphon solani* (Kaltenbach), *Aphis fabae* Scopoli, *Betulaphis quadrituberculata* (Kaltenbach), *Macrosiphum euphorbiae* (Thomas), and *Myzus persicae* (Sulzer).

Entomophthora thaxteriana (Petch) Hall and Bell 1963

Syn. *Empusa planchoniana* (Cornu ?) Thaxter 1888; *Empusa thaxteriana* Petch 1937; *Entomophthora ignobilis* Hall and Dunn 1957.

Conidia: globose to almost spherical, with papillate base, and contents quite granular and dense; 21-34 μ in diameter (exclusive of base), average 31 μ (measurements reported by Gustafsson (1965) were slightly smaller, averaging 29 μ in diameter). The secondary conidia are like the primary forms. *Conidiophores:* unbranched, quite often with only a few extending through the host integument. *Hyphal Bodies:* short, thick sections of hyphae, often branched or twisted; with rounded ends; 10-15 μ thick x 50-60 μ (or more) in length. *Cystidia:* absent. *Resting Spores:* spherical; thick-walled; smooth epispore; usually zygospores (with few azygospores noted); 23-50 μ in diameter, average 35 μ (Gustafsson (1965) reports an average of 37 μ in one case). *Host Attachment:* rhizoids absent; attachment by insertion of the proboscis.

Natural hosts of *E. thaxteriana* include *Acyrthosiphon pisum* (Harris), *A. solani* (Kaltenbach), *Aphis fabae* Scopoli, *A. gossypii* Glover, *A. nasturtii* Kaltenbach, *Euceraphis punctipennis* (Zest.), *Marcrosiphum euphorbiae* (Thomas), *Microlophium evansi* (Theobald), *Myzus persicae* (Sulzer), *Nasonovia lactucae* (Linnaeus), *Rhopalomyzus lonicerae* (Siebold), *Rhopalosiphoninus staphyleae* (Koch), *Rhopalosiphum padi* (Linnaeus), and *Schizaphis graminum* (Rondani).

In addition, Krejzova (1972) reports that *Aphis forbesi* Weed and *Megoura viciae* Buckton have been found to be experimentally susceptible to the fungus.

Entomophthora virulenta Hall and Dunn 1957

Conidia: globose to spherical, with papillate base and granulate interior; 17-18 μ in diameter (exclusive of papilla), average 22 μ. Secondary conidia like the primary forms. *Conidiophores:* unbranched and forming a dense reddish covering over the host body. *Hyphal Bodies:* short sections of hyphae of irregular shape, often branched or twisted; 8-12 μ thick x 40-60 μ (or more) in length. *Cystidia:* occur rarely. *Resting Spores:* generally spherical; thick-walled, smooth epispore, one to several large vacuoles in granular cytoplasm; 15-30 μ in diameter, average 22 μ. The original description states that they were generally azygospores, with some zygospores. However, Gustafsson (1965) indicates that they are zygospores. *Host Attachment: rhizoids.*

Natural aphid hosts of *E. virulenta* are *Myzodium modestum* (Hottes) and *Therioaphis maculata* (Buckton). In addition, *Aphis fabae* Scopoli, *A. gossypii* Glover and *Megoura viciae* Buckton have been found to be experimentally susceptible (Krejzova, 1972).

Gustafsson (1965) mentions an *Entomophthora neri* Rudraiah and Usman 1955 as being another species of fungus that attacks aphids. Careful check of the paper by Rudraiah and Usman (1955), however, reveals that this is in error, since they merely reported the occurrence of an epizootic in populations of *Aphis nerii* Fonscolombe in India caused by an *Entomophthora* sp. that was not further identified. Moreover, their sketchy presentation of the life stages of the fungus is inadequate for species determination. It would appear that the name *Entomophthora neri* is invalid.

In addition to the host data so far presented, there is a recent report by Krejzova (1972) that indicates that *Entomophthora destruens* Weiser and Batko, an isolate from *Culex pipiens* Linnaeus, has been determined to be experimentally pathogenic to *Aphis fabae* Scopoli and *Megoura viciae* Buckton.

Ten of the 13 naturally pathogenic species of entomophthoraceous fungi reported herein appear to occur exclusively in aphids. Of this specific group, from the standpoint of known hosts and the diagnostic records of the author from examinations of dead, diseased aphids submitted from varied parts of the world, the most common and widespread species is *E. aphidis* Hoffmann, followed by *E. thaxteriana* (Petch) and *E. planchoniana* Cornu. The three species showing nonspecificity are *E. coronata, E. sphaerosperma,* and *E. virulenta,* of which *E. sphaerosperma* probably is the most important in its activity against aphids, although it has rarely been diagnosed by this author.

Literature on entomophthoraceous fungi parasitizing aphids in New Zealand is meagre with only the reports of Lowe (1963, 1968) indicating that *Entomophthora aphidis* Hoffmann causes epizootics in field populations of *Brevicoryne brassicae* (Linnaeus) on cole crops. Other fungus-aphid host relationships determined by this author while in Nelson in 1963 include: *E. aphidis* on *Aulacorthum solani* (Kaltenbach) (on clover collected at Brookside), *Cavariella aegopodii* (Scopoli) (on yarrow at Nelson), and *Myzus ornatus* Laing (on *Hypericum decorum* at Nelson); *E. planchoniana* Cornu on *C. aegopodii* (on yarrow at Nelson) and *Macrosiphum rosae* (Linnaeus) (on rose at Nelson); and *E. thaxteriana* Petch on *Myzus ornatus* (on *H. decorum* at Nelson).

REFERENCES

Charles, V. K. 1941. A preliminary check list of the entomogenous fungi of North America. *U.S.D.A. Bur. Entomol. & Plant Quarant., Insect Pest Survey Bull., Suppl. to No. 9,* 21: 707-785.

Fresenius, G. 1856. Notiz, Insekten-Pilze betreffend. *Bot. Ztg.* 14: 882-883.

Grobler, J. H., MacLeod, D. M. and De Lyzer, A. J. 1962. The fungus *Empusa aphidis* Hoffman parasitic on the woolly pine needle aphid, *Schizolachnus piniradiatae* (Davidson). *Can Ent.* 94: 46-49.

Gustafsson, M. 1965. On species of the genus *Entomophthora* Fres. in Sweden. I. Classification and Distribution. *Lantbrukshägsk. Ann.* 31: 103-212.

—— 1971. Microbial control of aphids and scale insects. *In* "Microbial Control of Insects and Mites" (H. D. Burgess and N. W. Hussey, eds.), pp. 375-384. Academic Press, London and New York.

Hall, I. M., and Bell, J. V. 1963. The synonymy of *Empusa thaxteriana* Petch and *Entomophthora ignobilis* Hall and Dunn. *J. Insect Path.,* 5: 182-186.

Hall, I. M., and Dunn, P. H. 1957. Entomophthorous fungi parasitic on the spotted alfalfa aphid. *Hilgardia* 27: 159-181.

Kevorkian, A. G. 1937. Studies in the Entomophthoraceae. I. Observations on the genus *Conidiobolus, J. Agric. Univ. Puerto Rico* 21: 191-200.

Krejzova, R. 1972. Experimental infections of several species of aphids by specimens of the genus *Entomophthora. Věst. Čs. spol. zool.* 36: 17-22.

Leatherdale, D. 1958. A host catalogue of British entomogenous fungi. *Entomologist's mon. Mag.* 94: 103-105.

—— 1970. The arthropod hosts of entomogenous fungi in Britain. *Entomophaga* 15: 419-435.

Lee, P. 1965. Viruslike particles in the salivary glands of apparently virus-free leafhoppers. *Virology* 25: 471.

Lowe, A. D. 1963. The fungus *Entomophthora aphidis* Hoffman parasitic on the cabbage aphid *Brevicoryne brassicae (L)* in New Zealand. *N.Z. Jl. agric. Res.* 6: 314-317.

—— 1968. The incidence of parasitism and disease in some populations of the cabbage aphid *(Brevicoryne brassicae (L.))* in New Zealand. *N.Z. Jl. agric. Res.* 11: 821-828.

Macleod, D. M. 1955. A fungus enemy of the pea aphid, *Macrosiphum pisi (Kaltenbach). Can. Ent.* 87: 503-505.

—— 1963. Entomophthorales infections. *In* "Insect Pathology An Advanced Treatise". (E. A. Steinhaus, ed.), Vol. 2, pp. 189-231. Academic Press, New York and London.

Moericke, V. 1963. Uber "Virusartige Körper" in organen von *Myzus persicae* (Sulz.). *Z. Pflanzenkrankh. Pflanzenschutz* 70: 464-470.

Nolla, J. A. B. 1929. *Acrostalagmus aphidum* Oud., and aphid control. *J. Dept. Agr. Porto Rico,* 13: 59-72.

Parrish, W. B., and Briggs, J. D. 1966. Morphological identification of viruslike particles in the corn leaf aphid, *Rhopalosiphum maidis* (Fitch). *J. Invertebrate Path.,* 8: 122-123.

Petch, T. 1932. Notes on Entomogenous fungi. *Trans. Brit. Mycol. Soc.* 16: 209-245.

—— 1937. Notes on Entomogenous fungi. *Trans. Brit. Mycol. Soc.* 21: 34-67.

—— 1948. A revised list of British entomogenous fungi. *Trans. Brit. Mycol. Soc.* 31: 286-304.

Rudraiah, M. P., and Usman, S. 1955. An epizootic of the oleander aphids. *Sci. and Culture* 21: 158-159.

Schaefer, E. E. 1941. A fungus of the family Entomophthoraceae found on sugar ants *(Campanotus* sp.). *Bothalia* 4: 237-249.

Shands, W. A., Hall, I. M., and Simpson, G. W. 1962. Entomophthoraceous fungi attacking the potato aphid in northeastern Maine in 1960. *J. econ. Ent.* 55: 174-179.

Shands, W. A., Simpson, G. W., and Hall, I. M. 1963. Importance of entomogenous fungi in controlling aphids on potatoes in northeastern Maine. *Maine Agric. Expt. Sta. Bull.* T. 6 (Technical Series), pp. 1-42.

Shands, W. A., Simpson, G. W., Hall, I. M., and Gordon, C. C. 1972. Further evaluation of entomogenous fungi as a biological agent of aphid control in northeastern Maine. *Maine Agric. Expt. Sta. Tech. Bull,* 58, 33 pp.

Shands, W. A., Thompson, C. G., Simpson, G. W., and Wave, H. E. 1958. Preliminary studies of entomogenous fungi for the control of potato-infesting aphids in Maine. *J. econ. Ent.* 51: 184-186.

Soper, R. S., and Macleod, D. M. 1963. Spore morphology of *Entomophthora fresenii* Nowakowski. *J. Insect Path.* 5: 478-482.

Steinhaus, E. A. and Marsh, G. A. 1962. Report of diagnoses of diseased insects 1951-1961. *Hilgardia* 33: 349-490.

Thaxter, R. 1888. The entomophthoraceae of the United States. *Mem. Boston Soc. Nat. Hist.* 4: 133-201.

Thoizon, G. 1967. *Entomophthora pyriformis,* sp. n., Entomophthorale parasite de puceron. *Entomophaga* 12: 303-307.

Wolcott, G. N. 1955. Experiences with entomogenous fungi in Puerto Rico. *Univ. Puerto Rico Agric. Expt. Sta. Bull.* 130: 1-19.

BIOTYPES OF APHIDS

By V. F. Eastop

British Museum (Natural History), Cromwell Road, London, S.W. 7

1. *Definition*

'Biotype' is a taxonomic concept mostly used by non-taxonomists and has been defined as consisting of all individuals of equal genotype. As each fundatrix of an aphid arises from a different fertilised egg, each is the foundress of a distinct, parthenogenetically propagated clone. The existence of clones is inherent in organisms with successive parthenogenetic generations. The word 'clone' already exists for this concept and there is no advantage in replacing it by 'biotype'. In aphids at least, and probably elsewhere, 'equal genotype' means 'behaving similarly as far as the researcher's immediate interests are concerned'. Some genotypes are more equal than others.

Biotypes are recognised by a biological function rather than by morphological characters. In practice a biotype contains those individuals performing whatever biological feat interests the observer and thus may contain one or more races or strains (van Emden et al, 1969). Those individuals able to feed on a normally pest-resistant variety of cultivated plant may be regarded as belonging to one biotype. The ability to feed on this variety of plant may be conferred by a single gene and thus all individuals with this allele will constitute the biotype. In cases like this, part of the progeny of one female may belong to one biotype and part to another. Biotypes are not necessarily mutually exclusive. An individual or clone may belong to two or more biotypes. For instance it could belong to a host-plant resistance breaking biotype as the result of an allele of a gene on one chromosome and to an insecticide resistant biotype as the result of an allele of a gene on the same or a different chromosome. The taxonomic status of the characters by which aphid biotypes are recognised is equivalent in some respects to eye colour in human beings: and sometimes perhaps with hair colour in that the biotypic status may change with age.

The taxonomic implications are that when a biotype first appears it may be morphologically recognisable since it is likely to occur only in one clone. If the gene spreads through the population and occurs in different genotypes, not all the individuals possessing the relevant allele(s) are likely to be morphologically detectable. A similar biological effect may be achieved by different genetical means and an apparent biotype may be created on a number of occasions by mutations of the same or different genes. Biological characters such as host plant preferences, susceptibilities to insecticides, etc., tend to be a matter of degree or to depend on the temperature at which a particular enzyme system is activated. They are comparable to the deposition of pigment which although often useful in taxonomy must be treated with caution. In situations like these it is best to avoid the term 'biotype' and to use the word 'population' or at least 'biotypes' in the plural.

2. *History of the concept of 'biotype'*

The concept of morphological and colour varieties within a species is almost as old as taxonomy. For instance, Walker (1850) described 21 apterous varieties of *Myzus persicae*. The fact that some of these alleged varieties are eventually assigned to other species does not affect the antiquity of the concept. Although 'biotype' is a fairly new word the basic concept is more than 100 years old. Walsh (1864) writing of phytophagous insects recognised what he called 'phytophagic varieties', but he did not mention any aphids. Cholodkovsky (1908) working with adelgids, used the term 'biological species' for populations which he regarded as distinct species because of their different biologies. Numerous authors have recognised 'races' and 'strains' of aphids. More recently the term 'biotype' has become more fashionable.

There are several reasons for the changing terminology in sub-specific taxonomy. The concepts have been modified through the years to reflect what successive generations of biologists have thought most relevant to the situation in nature. Present sub-specific concepts are likely to consider the amount of gene flow between populations and the sort of reproductive barriers existing between populations, whether physical, behavioural or cytological. Each step in sophistication of the concept of reproductive barriers has required a new terminology to distinguish it from the concepts of the previous generation. The concepts of the previous generations have been abandoned not only because of their naivety but also because of an occupational hazard inherent in taxonomy. The poorer the observations and experiments, the more likely are spurious taxa to be described. This tends to discredit the taxonomic concept used and provides an added impetus for it to appear in a more sophisticated guise under another name.

Many biotypes and biological species, said to be inseparable by their original authors, have proved to be perfectly separable by using newer techniques of preparation. In other cases it has not been possible to confirm the biological separations claimed. Absence of controls from the experimental work was probably the commonest fault.

Terms such as 'biotype' and 'biological species' tend to be used more by people interested in experimental work and particularly by people principally interested in one aspect of a species, for instance its host plant range, virus transmitting ability or susceptibility to insecticides. Taxonomists tend to think more of geographically isolated sub-species and races, and in terms of gene flow between populations. Neither concept is complete without the other, and this is particularly important in the case of pests which are often pests just because of their biological plasticity.

Nevertheless there are many real taxonomic concepts in aphids for which the term biotype is useful, as long as it is not assumed to be equivalent to 'race' or 'strain' in every respect.

3. *Examples of biotypes*

Most of the aphids which have been carefully and intensively studied have been found to consist of a complex of biotypes. These biotypes have been recognised by a variety of characters, including differences in life cycles, reaction to light, different host plant preferences, different virus transmitting abilities, different feeding behaviour and differential susceptibility to insecticides. Some of these populations have also been characterised by morphology or colour.

The pea aphid, *Acyrthosiphon pisum* (Harris) contains many populations to which the term biotype is properly applied. Eastop (1971) gave references to 12 papers concerning 'races' of *A. pisum*. F. P. Müller (1971) gave the results of breeding experiments with subspecies and races of *A. pisum*, with special reference to the isolating mechanisms between sympatric populations. *Acyrthosiphon pelargonii* (Klt.) (= *malvae*) is a member of a complex of populations differing in biology and in some cases at least in morphology. Stroyan (1964) has summarised the present state of knowledge. An anholocyclic race of *Acyrthosiphon (Metopolophium) festucae* (Theobald) was described by F. P. Müller (1968).

The genetical basis of host plant resistance breaking in populations of *Amphorophora rubi* (Kltb.) has been described by Briggs (1965).

F. P. Müller (1966) regards the tropical pest of Leguminosae, *Aphis craccivora* Koch, as an anholocyclic population of a holocyclic European species. The *Aphis fabae* group contains similar-looking populations with different biologies but in the confused taxonomic state of the group terms like 'biotype' have no precise meaning. The *Aphis gossypii* Glover group is equally confusing taxonomically but in *A. gossypii* itself Boyce (1938) recorded the existence of a population resistant to HCN and later authors have found populations resistant to BHC (Herrera Arunguena, 1958) and to Systox (Chang and Zhong, 1966). Simons (1958, 1959) recorded the existence of strains of *A. gossypii* with different virus-transmitting abiliites.

F. P. Müller (1969) has described a population of *Aphis nasturtii* Kltb. which prefers *Calla* to potato as a secondary host plant but both populations alternate from *Rhamnus*.

F. P. Müller (1970) gave an account of host plant transference experiments with populations of *Aulacorthum solani* (Kltb.). He recognised a number of polyphagous populations and several monophagous subspecies.

A strain of *Brevicoryne brassicae* (L.) which colonised previously resistant varieties of crops was recorded by Lammerink (1968) and Cognetti (1965) recognised different strains by their biologies.

An anholocyclic srain of *Cavariella aegopodii* (Scop.) has been recorded by F. P. Müller (1966).

Endosulphan resistant populations of *Chaetosiphon fragaefolii* (Cockerell) have been found by Shansk (1967).

Organophosphorus-resistant populations of *Chromaphis juglandicola* (Kltb.) have been recorded from California (Brown, 1961).

Hille Ris Lambers (1953) recognised three subspecies of *Cryptomyzus galeopsidis* (Kltb.), all holocyclic but one with host alternation and the other two confined to species of *Ribes*.

Shaposhnikov (1965) grew his own strain of *Dysaphis anthrisci* s-sp. *majkopica* by progressive transfers to less acceptable host plants, ending with a population which would not accept the original host.

Giliomée, Stryden & Van Zyl (1968) have found populations of the woolly apple aphid, *Eriosoma lanigerum* (Hausm.) which can colonise previously resistant varieties of apples.

The anholocyclic tropical populations of *Lipaphis erysimi* (Kltb.) are regarded as races of the European holocyclic species by F. P. Müller (1966).

Shull (1932, 1943) records a sudden change in 1929 in response to exposure to light by a population of *Macrosiphum euphorbiae* (Thomas) with which he had been working for several years. After 1929 the colony bred true for its new response for nearly 10 years until the experiment was discontinued.

Cognetti (1966) writes about the races of *Macrosiphum rosae* (L.). Occasional bright yellow specimens of the usually bright green aphid, *Megoura viciae* have appeared in experimental cultures and these have continued to produce yellow young.

Van Emden et al. (1969) gave 40 references to biotypes and races of *Myzus persicae,* and Blackman (1971) has given accounts of the biologies of clones derived from specimens collected on different crops and at different localities, with special reference to the proportions of different biotypes found on different crops.

Insecticide resistant populations of *Phorodon humuli* (Schrank) have been recorded by Hrdy and Zeleny (1963), and later authors.

Printz (1937) has given an account of the races of *Viteus vitifoliae* (Fitch) (= *Phylloxera vastatrix*).

An anholocyclic population of the usually obligatorily holocyclic *Rhopalosiphum insertum* (Walker) has been recorded. Cartier & Painter (1956), Painter (1958), Painter & Pathack (1962), and Pathack & Painter (1958, 1959) give accounts of the food plant preferences of the biotypes of *Rhopalosiphum maidis* (Fitch). A population of *Rhopalosiphum padi* (L.) in which hot weather dwarfs had both an unusual wing venation and an increased virus transmitting ability was described by Rochow & Eastrop (1966).

Tropical populations of *Schizaphis graminum* (Rondani) have been regarded as distinct races by Müller (1966) and the 'sorghum green bug' which spread across much of western North America in 1968 was probably the result of the introduction of a previously absent genotype.

A similar thing happened with the 'spotted alfalfa aphid' and this insect, *Therioaphis trifolii* f. *maculata* (Buckton), has subsequently given rise to populations with increased insecticide resistance (Stern, 1962).

British populations of *Toxoptera aurantii* (B. de F.) have been found only on camellia while the aphid lives on shrubs belonging to many families in the tropics. These British populations may represent only part of the genetical make-up of the species and thus constitute a biotype.

4. *Sources of biotypes*

One of the simplest sources of biotypes is the introduction into an area of one clone of a species. The resultant population will have only part of the genetical potential of the species and may have a more restricted biology than the parent species, e.g. the British populations of *Toxoptera aurantii* which are found only on camellia. If a second but genetically incompatible or behaviourally isolated clone is introduced, the two populations may behave as though they belonged to distinct species, e.g. the yellow clover aphid, *Therioaphis trifolii* (Monell) and the spotted alfalfa aphid, *T. trifolii* f. *maculata* (Buckton) (Hille Ris Lambers & van den Bosch, 1964). The interaction between the 'green bug', *Schizaphis graminum* and the 'sorghum green bug' will be interesting. Introduction is not the usual source of biotypes.

Biotypes are better known in aphids than in many other families of insects. This is not (only) a reflection on the standard of taxonomy. There are aspects of the biology of aphids which predispose them to the production of biotypes. The course of development of a species depends partly on what happens to its environment and the selection pressures acting on it, and partly on the genetical factors intrinsic to the group to which it belongs. Most new taxa have been formed by interruptions in the gene flow within parent species. The simplest case is perhaps geographical separation and resultant genetic drift and different selection pressures. The best known cases are the island faunas of small mammals, etc. The essence is that the gene flow has been interrupted by restricting meetings between individuals of the two populations to an insignificant level. The mobility of the organisms must be small compared to the barriers between them. In some wingless organisms a stream a few yards wide may constitute such a barrier. The nature of the barrier may not be evident to a human observer. Some subspecies of actively flying butterflies such as blues have adjacent territories delimited by barriers that seem to present no physical difficulty. Nevertheless the barrier apparently prevents interbreeding. These situations have little direct agricultural importance, for it is difficult to imagine a species that could not cross a stream or a hedge, becoming a pest.

The winged forms of many aphids fly up towards the sky and may be displaced for many miles before they settle on a plant. The result is that an aphid population at one place is not or is only partially descended from the population that occurred there the previous year. Aphids are vagile. That is, they are not only mobile, but progeny develop well away from the place where their mother developed. The result is that complexes of geographically isolated species and subspecies of aphids are seldom described. The isolating mechanisms in the evolution of aphids has often been host plant specificity and it is no coincidence that many biotypes of aphids have been recognised by their host plant preferences.

Dickson (1959) showed that at peak flight periods 133,000,000 aphids per minute may pass a one mile front which is two miles from the source of the aphids. On another occasion when 8,800,000 aphids were passing a one mile front Dickson calculated that 6,000 aphids should have been visiting each cantaloupe plant on the farm during a three hour period. Observation showed that 9,000 green peach aphids visited each plant during the three hour period. He also discovered that 75 miles of desert was not an effective barrier to aphids. It is thus virtually impossible to have a polyphagous aphid consisting of numerous geographically isolated sub-species. Nevertheless there is some geographically induced genetical isolation in aphids, partly due to the continuous selection of biotypes that can survive at the often mobile extremities of the range of a species and strongly reinforced by the tendency of the warmer environments to select populations that produce fewer sexuales. Some movement is probably largely one way, due to prevailing seasonal winds. Enormous populations of *Myzus persicae* leave the peach trees of southern Europe every spring and early summer but the pattern of winds in the Mediterranean suggests that the most active dispersers may contribute least to the return migration in the autumn. However, the widespread insecticide resistance in *Myzus persicae* on peach during recent years suggests that the population on peach each year is descended from the previous year's population.

Another interruption in the gene flow between populations of aphids is caused by the existence of two year cycles. There are species of both aphids and psyllids in which a particular population produces sexuales in alternate years. This type of cycle occurs in both Fordini and Adelgidae. In aphids there is probably a large enough residue each year on the secondary host to contribute to the following years gene pool and thus prevent the genetical isolation of the two populations. The situation is comparable to that of other Hemiptera in which univoltine and bivoltine populations occur in the same species or two generations occur out of phase (Whalley, 1972). In all these situations the combination of movement of individuals to different climatic conditions and the effect of occasional very hot and very cold years, probably result in gene flow between the normally isolated populations.

The great dispersive activity, or vagility, of most aphids is an inherent factor which has influenced their evolution, in several different but connected ways. At some times of the year aphids are showered down on to the vegetation in enormous numbers (Johnson, 1969). The great majority of aphids are host specific and even the 'polyphagous' species have evident host plant preferences. There are many common plants that are not or only rarely colonised by 'polyphagous' aphids such as *Aphis fabae* and *Myzus persicae*. Even when these species are common there are more plants without colonies than with them. Most species of aphids are specific to one or several closely related plants, but about 10% of the species of aphids alternate between members of two botanically distinct groups of plants and other sorts of discontinuous host plant preferences are known. Nutritionally suitable host plants botanically distant from the normal hosts of an aphid and its close relatives have been called 'reserve hosts' by Stroyan (1963). *Capsella bursa-pastoris* is a member of the Cruciferae, but *Acyrthosiphon pisum* which normally feeds on Leguminosae, *Amphorophora rubi* which normally feeds on Rosaceae and *Macrosiphum avenae* and *M. miscanthi* which normally feed on Gramineae, may all form colonies on *Capsella*.

Host plant specificity has formed the basis of much aphid speciation (Eastop, 1972). There are aphid species in which the ecological niche is not primarily based on host plant specificity, but they are rare. Many biotypes of aphids have been distinguished by their differing host plant preferences and to understand the nature and origin of biotypes we must study the origin and nature of host plant specificity. The great majority of aphids are host specific at some level. No aphid has been recorded from even 1% of all the species of flowering plants. Most aphids feed on only a few species of related plants. More than half the described species of aphids are specific to members of one plant genus. About 10% of aphids alternate seasonally between one or a few species of primary host plants and one or more secondary host plants. These host alternating species of aphids have on average a greater host plant range in the summer than aphids without host plant alternation. Of the 445 European Aphidinae without host plant alternation, 407 (91%), have their host plants confined to a single genus. Of the 141 heteroecious European Aphidinae, only 9, (6%) have their secondary hosts confined to one genus.

Aphids with host plant alternation and the other species with discontinuous host plant preferences cannot be arranged in any order indicating that the primitive aphid was polyphagous and that all the other groups of plants have been lost from the host range during the course of evolution. In a few cases the discontinuous hosts of an aphid species have been shown to contain the same distinctive chemical, e.g. sinigrin in both Cruciferae and *Tropaeolum*, hosts of the cabbage aphid, *Brevicoryne brassicae* (L.). Weisman & Halenda (1968) associate large *Aphis fabae* with high concentrations of asparagine and arginine. Similar patterns of discontinuous host plant preferences are found in different orders of insects but this

45

may indicate either the presence of similar constituents or of a spatial or historical similarity.

While most members of a group of aphids occur on a particular taxonomic group of plants, exceptions are not uncommon. Most species of *Myzocallis* and close relatives live on Fagaceae, Betulaceae and close relatives, but *Myzocallis asclepiadis* lives on *Asclepias* of the Asclepiadaceae. Ferns are populated by several genera of aphids which have their closest relatives on Rosaceae. For these and other reasons (Eastop, 1972), is thought that most aphids acquired their present host plants by capture rather than by evolution with that group of plants. Host plant specificity in aphids arose because aphids evolved on flowering plants, not as parasitic prisoners, but as free-living organisms colonising new environments. Aphids and psyllids are specific to particular species of plants because specificity acted as an isolating mechanism in the early stages of evolution, isolating the new species from its progenitors, and in the later stages, host plant specificity maintains genetical variability and hence evolutionary potential, by causing each species of aphid to live in numerous partly isolated populations. These populations may represent biotypes. Whatever the cause of host plant specificity, it is a fact of life, and it is not surprising to find that host specificity features largely in the recognition of aphid biotypes. This is almost inevitable by definition. Members of morphologically distinct populations with different biologies have already been distinguished as distinct species by classical taxonomy. Populations of similar appearance but different biology are defined as biotypes. The aspect of the biology of an aphid which interests most people is the range of plants upon which it will feed.

The thesis is that aphid biotypes acquired their present host plants comparatively recently. The yellow form of *Acyrthosiphon pisum* on *Lotus corniculatus* did not get there by differentiating with the Leguminosae as the genera evolved, but the genotype which could accept *Lotus* was produced on some other legume. This chicken came before the egg. New biotypes appear almost literally out of the blue, according to Moericke (1955a, b) and Kennedy & Booth (1954).

The parthenogenetic generations of aphids also exhibit polymodal variation (= polymorphism). A mechanism for the temporary inactivation of part of the genetical code is a prerequisite for a parthenogenetic polymorphic organism, as is a mechanism for its reactivation. A long-delayed reactivation may be the cause of the reticulum of morphological characters observed in groups where continuous parthenogenesis and polymorphism are common. The mechanism is presumably a system of suppressor genes. In aphids the course of evolution can be reversed. Suppressions and less delayed reactivations may be the causes of some of the changes within clones. This genetical system tends to make biotypes unstable, and since by definition members of a biotype have equal genotype, it tends to increase the number of biotypes.

5. *Economic problems posed by biotypes*

The existence of biotypes makes the host range and insecticide susceptibility of a population less predictable. Varieties of plants previously resistant to aphids may suddenly become colonised, e.g. *Amphorophora rubi* on raspberries in England (Briggs, 1965) and *Schizaphis graminum* on sorghum in America (Anon., 1969). There are records of insecticide resistant biotypes for at least eight different species of aphids. Such biotypes present problems for both plant breeders and chemists.

The 'strains' of parasitic fungi have provided work for plant breeders for some time and there is a risk that aphids will do the same if serious attempts are made to breed more insecticide resistance into crops. The following cases of insecticide resistance in aphids are recorded.

Aphid	Product	Authority
Aphis gossypii	H.C.N.	Boyce, 1928
Aphis gossypii	Organophosphorus	Chang & Zhong, 1966
Aphis gossypii	B.H.C.	Brown, 1958
Neomyzus circumflexus	B.H.C.	Brown, 1958
Macrosiphum euphorbiae	D.D.T.	Brown, 1958
Chaetosiphon fragaefolii	Endosulphan	Shansk, 1967
Dysaphis plantaginea	Organophosphorus	Brown, 1961
Dysaphis pyri	Organophosphorus	Brown, 1961
Myzus cerasi	Organophosphorus	Brown, 1961
Myzus persicae	Organophosphorus	Anthon, 1955 and many others
Phorodon humuli	Organophosphorus	Hrdy & Zeleny, 1968
Chromaphis juglandicola	Organophosphorus	Michelbacher *et al.* 1959
Therioaphis trifolii f. maculata	Organophosphorus	Klostermeyer *et al.* 1956
Rhodobium porosum	Carbamate	

When the insecticide pressure is taken off the insecticide resistance may be lost (Dunn & Kempton, 1966). The problems for biological control arise from the almost infinite number of biotypes of an aphid species, differing slightly from one another both morphologically and physiologically. Different biotypes of an aphid species are likely to differ in habitat (different biotypes having different optima), or virus transmitting abilities, and their life processes generally may be circumscribed by different parameters. One biotype may develop at a temperature below the threshold of activity for a predator while another will not.

The effect of new biotypes is not always deleterious to the grower. Winged individuals of an anholocyclic biotype arriving on a crop are likely to contain eggs of parasites which will remain in that crop, while parasites developing from eggs acquired on a primary host may be adapted to searching trees and shrubs for their aphid hosts. The loss from the life cycle of the primary host has many other implications for control including the availability of large numbers of alatae early in the year, which developed on plants which may be infected with viruses unlikely to be acquired by aphids originating from a primary host plant.

6. *Taxonomy of biotypes*

Morphology is the end product of physiological activities, initiated by the genome and modified by environment. A change in physiology in the immature stage is likely to result in a change in morphology, the problem being to detect it among the many other factors affecting the eventual appearance of an organism. In practice almost any two clones of aphids are separable from one another because the variation of most characters within each clone will be small. As large numbers of specimens from each clone are usually easy to obtain, small differences between the means can be highly significant. It is not usually possible to recognise biotypes in field collections since these often consist of a mixture of a number of biotypes in unknown proportions.

Although most characters are usually constant within similar-sized individuals of one clone, some characters may show the whole variation known for that species

47

within one clone. The ultimate rostral segment of *Myzus persicae* may bear from 2 to 7 hairs in the progeny of one parthenogenetic female, which is the variation known for the species throughout the world. The sub-genital plate of *M. persicae* bears only two hairs on the anterior half almost constantly. The ultimate rostral segment of *Macrosiphum avenae* bears 6 accessory hairs almost constantly, while the anterior half of the sub-genital plate may bear from 2 to 6 hairs in the progeny of a single female, which is again the variation known for the species over the whole of its geographical range. This variation within clones complicates the morphological recognition of biotypes especially if similar variation also occurs in behavioural characters.

Aphids are so much affected by environmental conditions that one year's population increase is often different from the previous year's pattern. The weather early in the spring is likely also to have had many indirect effects, including the selection of some biotypes at the expense of others. The pattern of biotypes is likely to differ from year to year due to changes in weather and from field to field due to local conditions. Unless quickly detectable morphological characters can be found which are linked with economically important characters of each biotype, there is little advantage to be obtained by studying their taxonomy. The existence of biotypes is one of the reasons why aphids can be so unpredictable.

7. *Nomenclature of biotypes*

As biotypes are temporally unstable, numerically infinite and often difficult to detect morphologically, a system of nomenclature based on type specimens is inappropriate. However, it is difficult to think about a thing unless you have a name for it. Having a name implies distinguishing it from other similar concepts. The 'sorghum-feeding biotype' of the 'greenbug' is a valid name and concept as long as it is remembered that it is only a name given to those individuals that fed on sorghum during the course of the observations. There is no fundamental difference between recognising an organism by its appearance or by its behaviour. Both morphology and behaviour are a product of genetically initiated physiology modified by the environment. Morphology has the great advantage that it can be checked on dead specimens whereas there is always an element of hearsay about behaviour, and it may not be constant throughout the life of the individual. For these reasons a formal system of nomenclature does not seem appropriate. A descriptive system of nomenclature based on common names such as is used for plant viruses is likely to be most useful.

8. *Coping with existing biotypes*

The breeding of new resistant varieties of plants, the introduction of natural enemies also favouring the new habitat and pesticides will be used against aphids which colonise previously resistant varieties of crops. The development of new insecticides requiring different detoxification processes, attacks on the detoxification processes themselves, and possibly reinforcement of the plant's own protective devices (Dyte, 1967; van Emden, 1969), are likely to be used against insecticide resistant biotypes. Biotypes distinguished by characteristics not involved in crop protection should be dealt with by existing methods.

9. *Discouraging the production of new biotypes*

Economically important biotypes occur because of cultural selection pressures.

The uniformity of the crop environment reduces the number of mortality factors. A large part of the mortality may be caused by an insecticide or a large habitat may be protected by a single gene of a pest resistant crop variety. Most aphids are host specific, in other words, most species of plants are resistant to most species of aphids, and this specificity has lasted at least for several hundred years. Many common plants are regularly bombarded with common aphids, which seldom develop colonies on them. There are a number of reasons for the persistence of resistance. Resistance to insect attack is part of the evolutionary story of plants, just as overcoming the protective mechanisms of plants is part of the evolution of phytophagous insects. For instance, sticky hairs can make a plant unacceptable to many aphids but some seem to use the presence of sticky hairs as an arrestant. By giving a crop sticky hairs it may be protected from many aphids but made susceptible to a few others.

The answer to biotypes lies in the cliché of 'integrated control'; allowing the resistance of the plant, carefully timed and usually early application of insecticide and a number of different species of natural enemies to cause an appreciable part of each year's mortality.

CONCLUSIONS

Biotypes is a concept recognised by function before morphology. As the term is commonly used, a population may belong to more than one biotype and the progeny of a single female may contain members of more than one biotype. Biotype is an old concept in a more sophisticated guise. Most species of aphids which have been investigated have been found to consist of a complex of biotypes. Biotypes are inherent in the evolutionary system of aphids, with its environmentally induced morphs and vagile biology. The evolution of 'biotypes' is a consequence of the type of aphid life cycle consisting of an indefinite number of several parthenogenetic strains. The genetical system required for environmentally induced morphs evolved in order to cope with changing conditions by producing populations suited to the new environment. When the new environment consists of insecticides or resistant varieties of plants, the likely results are insecticide resistant or host plant resistance-breaking biotypes of aphids. Such biotypes are occurring all over the world at the moment. Biotypes present similar problems to chemists and to plant breeders; they also present problems to taxonomists. The agronomist can avoid the worst consequences of biotypes by diversifying the causes of mortality and the introduction of complex genetical resistance in plant varieties. The taxonomist can ignore their presence in the belief that they will go away.

REFERENCES

Anon. 1969. *Co-operative Economic Insect Report,* 19: 487.
Anthon, E. W. 1955. Evidence for green peach aphid resistance to organophosphorus insecticides. *J. econ. Ent.* 48: 56-57.
Blackman, R. L. 1971a. Variation in the photoperiodic response within natural populations of *Myzus persicae* (Sulz.). *Bull. ent. Res.* 60: 533-546.
——— 1971b. Chromosomal abnormalities in an anholocyclic biotype of *Myzus persicae* (Sulzer). *Experientia* 27: 704-706.
Boyce, A. M. 1928. Studies in the resistance of certain insects to hydrocyanic acid. *J. econ. Ent.* 21: 715-720.

Briggs, J. B. 1965. The distribution, abundance and genetic relationships of four strains of the rubus aphid *(Amphorophora rubi* (Kltb.) in relation to raspberry breeding. *J. hort. Sci.* 40: 109-117.

Brown, A. W. A. 1958. The spread of insecticide resistance in pest species. *Adv. Pest Control Res.* 2: 351-414.

—— 1961. The challenge of insecticide resistance. *Bull. ent. Soc. Amer.* 7: 6-19.

Cartier, J. J. and Painter, R. H. 1956. Differential reactions of two biotypes of the corn leaf aphid to resistant and susceptible varieties, hybrids, and selections of sorghums. *J. econ. Ent.* 49: 498-508.

Chang, G. S. and Zhong, T. S. 1966. Studies on Systox-resistance in various morphs of *Aphis gossypii* Glover. *Acta ent. Sin.* 15: 201-216 [In Chinese, see *R.A.E.* 55: 240-241].

Cholodkovsky, N. 1908. Zur Frage über die biologischen Arten. *Biol. Centralbl.* 28: 169-782.

Cognetti, G. 1965. Determination of reproductive categories in the life cycle of aphids. *Experientia* 21: 449-453.

—— 1966. Genotipi e ambiente nelle determinazione delle categorie riproduttive degli afidi. *Atti del VI Congress Nazionale Italiano di Entomologia Padova,* 11-14 Settembre 1965, pp. 7-23.

Dickson, R. C. 1959. Aphid dispersal over Southern California deserts. *Ann. ent. Soc. Am.* 52: 368-372.

Dunn, J. A. and Kempton, D. P. 1966. Non-stable resistance to demeton-methyl in a strain of *Myzus persicae. Entomologia exp. appl.* 9: 67-73.

Dyte, C. E. 1967. Possible new approach to the chemical control of plant feeding insects. *Nature* 216: 298.

Eastop, V. F. 1971. Keys for the identification of *Acyrthosiphon* (Hemiptera: Aphididae). *Bull. Br. Mus. nat. Hist. (Ent.)* 26: 1-115.

—— 1972. The evolution of the insect plant relationship: deductions from the present day host plants of aphids and related insects. *R. ent. Soc. Lond. Symposium* 6: 153-174.

Giliomee, J. H., Strydom, D. K. and Van Zyl, H. J. 1968. Northern Spy, Merton and Malling-Merton root-stocks susceptible to woolly aphid, *Eriosoma lanigerum,* in the Western Cape. *S. Afr. J. Agric. Sci.* 11: 183-186.

Herrera Aranguena, J. 1958. Resistencia de ciertas plagas del algodonero a los insecticidas orgánicos en el Valle de Canete. *Rev. peruana Ent. agric.* 1: 47-51.

Hille Ris Lambers, D. 1953. Contributions to a monograph of the Aphididae of Europe. V. *Temminckia* 9: 1-176.

Hille Ris Lambers, D. and van den Bosch, R. 1964. On the genus *Therioaphis* Walker, 1870, with descriptions of new species (Homoptera, Aphididae). *Zool. verhand.* 68: 1-47.

Hardy, I. and Zelany, J. 1968. Hop aphid *(Phorodon humuli)* resistant to thiometon. *Acta ent. bohemoslav.* 65: 183-187.

Johnson, C. G. 1969. *The Migration and Dispersal of Insects by Flight.* Methuen, London, xvii + 763 pp.

Kennedy, J. S. 1958. Physiological condition of the host-plant and susceptibility to aphid attack. *Entomologia exp. appl.* 1: 50-65.

Kennedy, J. S. and Booth, C. O. 1954. Host alteration in *Aphis fabae* Scop. II. Changes in the aphids. *Ann. appl. Biol.,* 41: 88-106.

Kennedy, J. S. and Stroyan, H. L. G. 1959. Biology of aphids. *A. Rev. Ent.* 4: 139-160.

Klostermeyer, E. C., Landis, B. J., Schopp, R. and Buther, L. I. 1956. Effect of systematic insecticides on green peach aphid populations on potatoes. *J. econ. Ent.* 49: 164-166.

Lammerink, J. 1968. A new biotype of cabbage aphid *(Brevicoryne brassicae* L.) on aphid resistant rape *(Brassica napus* L.) *N.Z. Jl. agric. Res.* 11: 341-344.

Michelbacher, A. E., Fullmer, O. H., Cassil, C. C. and Davis, C. S., 1954. Walnut aphid resistant to parathion in northern California. *J. econ. Ent.* 47: 366-367.

Moericke, V. 1955a. Über die Lebensgewohnheiten der geflügelten Blattläuse (Aphidina) unter besondere Berücksichtigung des verhaltens beim Landen. *Z. angew. Ent.* 37: 29191. 37: 29191.

—— 1955b. Über das Verhalten phytophagen Insekten während des Befallsflugs unter dem Einfluss von weissen flächen. *Z. Pflanzenkrankh. u. Pflanzenschutz* 62: 588-593.

Müller, F. P. 1966. Schädliche Blattläuse in den Tropen und Subtropen unter besonderer Berücksichtigung von Rassendifferenzlerungen. *Z. Angew. Ent.* 58: 76-82.

—— 1968. Eine rote holozyklische Rasse von *Metopolophium festucae* (Theobald, 1917) (Homoptera: Aphididae). *Z. angew. Ent.* 61: 131-141.

—— 1969. Eine bionomische Rasse von *Aphis nasturtii* Kaltenbach, welche die Kartoffel meidet. *Arch. pflanzenschutz* 5: 179-188.

———— 1970. Zucht- und Übertragungsversuche mit Populationen und Klonen der Grün-fleckigen Kartoffelblattlaus *Aulacorthum solani* (Kaltenbach, 1843) (Homoptera: Aphididae). *Deutsche Ent. Zeits.* 17: 259-270.

———— 1971. Isolationsmechanismen zwischen sympatrischen bionomischen Rassen am Beispiel der Erbsenblattlaus *Acyrthosiphon pisum* (Harris) (Homoptera: Aphididae). *Zool. Jb. Syst.* 98: 131-152.

Painter, R. H. 1958. A study of resistance to aphids in crop plants. *Proc. Intern. Congr. Entomol.*, 10, Montreal, 1956, 3: 451-458.

Painter, R. H. and Pathak, M .D. 1962. The distinguishing features and significance of the four biotypes of the corn leaf aphid, *Rhopalosiphum maidis* (Fitch). *Proc. Intern. Congr. Entomol.*, 11, Vienna, 1960, 2: 110-115.

Pathak, M. D. and Painter, R. H. 1958. Effect of the feeding of the four biotypes of the corn leaf aphid, *Rhopalosiphum maidis* (Fitch) on susceptible white Martin sorghum and Spartan barley plants. *Kans. Ent. Soc. Jour.* 31: 93-100.

———— 1959. Geographical distribution of the four biotypes of cornleaf aphid, *Rhopalosiphum maidis* (Fitch) in Kansas. *Kans. Acad. Sci. Trans.* 62: 1-8.

Printz, Y. I. 1937. Contribution to the question of the changes in the virulence of *Phylloxera* of different biotypes. *Plant Prot. Leningrad*, 12: 137-142.

Rochow, W. F. and Eastop, V. F. 1966. Variation within *Rhopalosiphum padi* and trans-mission of Barley Yellow Dwarf virus by clones of four aphid species. *Virology* 30: 286-296.

Shansk, C. H. 1967. Resistance of the Strawberry aphid to endosulphan in south western Washington. *J. econ. Ent.* 60: 968-970.

Shaposhnikov, G. K. 1965. Morphological divergence and convergence in the experiment with aphids (Homoptera, Aphidinae). *Ent. Obozr.* 44: 1-25.

Shull, A. F., 1932. Clonal differences and clonal changes in the aphid *Macrosiphum solanifolii. Amer. Nat.* 66: 385-419.

———— 1943. Origin of diverse strains of an aphid species within a limited area. *Mich. Acad. Sci. Arts Letters* 28: 425-431.

Simons, J. N. 1958. Vector efficiency of transmission of two pepper viruses as influenced by species and clone of aphid. *Phytopathology* 48: 397.

———— 1959. Variation in efficiency of aphid transmission of southern cucumber mosaic virus and potato Y virus in pepper. *Virology* 9: 612-623.

Stern, V. M. 1962. Increased resistance to organophosphorus insecticides in the partheno-genetic spotted alfalfa aphid, *Therioaphis maculata*, in California. *J. econ. Ent.* 55: 900-904.

Stroyan, H. L. G. 1963. *The British Species of Dysaphis Börner (Sappaphis auctt. nec Mats.)* Part II. The Subgenus *Dysaphis* sensu stricto. H.M.S.O., London, 119 pp.

Van Emden, H. F. 1969. Plant resistance to aphids induced by chemicals. *J. Sci. Fd. Agric.* 20: 385-387.

Van Emden, H. F., Eastop, V. F., Hughes, R. D. and Way, M. J. 1969. The ecology of *Myzus persicae. A. Rev. Ent* 14: 197-270.

Walker, F. 1850. Descriptions of aphids. *Ann Mag. Nat. Hist.* (2) 5: 14-28.

Walsh, B. D. 1864. On the phytophagous varieties and phytophagic species. *Proc. ent. Soc. Phil.* 3: 403: 430.

Weismann, L. and Halanda, S. 1968. The reaction of the black bean aphid *Aphis fabae* Scop. to qualitative changes in the contents of amino acids in the vegetative organs of spindle *(Euonymus europaeus)* and seed sugar-beet plants. *Biologia, Bratislava* 23: 849-856.

Whalley, P. E. S. 1972. The effect of temperature on the development and diapause of the eggs of leaf-hoppers (Hem.: Auchenorhyncha), with notes on its ecological effects. *Entomologist's mon. Mag.* 108: 249-253.

POLYMORPHISIM IN APHIDS

By Louise M. Russell

Agricultural Research Service, U.S. Department of Agriculture, Washington, D.C. 20250 USA

ABSTRACT

Over the years the interpretation of the meaning of polymorphism in aphids has gradually changed from the recognition of differences in biology to consideration of diversity in every aspect of the insects development. The study of polymorphism has evolved from comparatively simple investigations of holocyclic and anholocyclic development and the appearance of winged and wingless forms to sophisticated studies of the environmental, morphological and physiological features that are responsible for the diversity that exists in the biology, morphology and habits of aphids.

Some studies have dealt with the complex seasonal development of sexual and asexual generations of heteroecious and monoecious species, and other studies have shown that, under certain conditions, numerous parthenogenetic generations can occur without the intervention of sexual ones. Other investigations have probed the development of winged and wingless morphs. A few studies have touched upon the effect of parasitism on the host aphid, and the possible presence of symbionts within specimens. The more recent experimental studies have concentrated on the role of temperature, photoperiod, nutrition, parentage, and endocrine action in the production or appearance of various forms. The literature on polymorphism in aphids is voluminous.

REFERENCES

Bonnemaison, L. 1951. Contribution a l'etude des facteurs provoquant l' apparition des formes ailées et sexuées chez les Aphidinae. *Ann. Epiphyt* 2: 1-280.

—— 1971. Action de la maturité de la plante-hote et de l'effect de groupe sur la production des virginopares ailées chez le puceron du pois *Acyrthosiphon pisum. Ann. Soc. Ent. France* (n. s.) 7 (4): 889-913.

Dadd, R. H. 1968. Dietary amino acids and wing determination in the aphid, *Myzus persicae. Ann. ent. Soc. Amer.* 61: 1201-1210.

Essig, E. O. and Abernathy, F. 1952. The aphid genus *Periphyllus.* Univ. of Calif. Press, Berkeley, 166 pp.

Ewing, H. E. 1916. Eighty seven generations in a parthenogenetic pure line of *Aphis avenae* Fab. *Biol. Bull.* 31: 53-112.

Hille Ris Lambers, D. 1960. Some notes on morph determination in aphids. *Ent. Bericht.* 20: 110-113.

—— 1966. Polymorphism in Aphididae. *A. Rev. Ent.* 11: 47-78.

Johnson, B. 1965. Wing polymorphism in aphids. II. Interaction between aphids. *Entomologia exp. appl.* 8: 49-64.

—— 1966. Wing polymorphism in aphids. III. The influence of the host plant. *Entomologia exp. appl.* 9: 213-222.

Johnson, B. and Birks, P. R. 1960. Studies on wing polymorphism in aphids. I. The developmental process involved in the production of the different forms. *Entomologia exp. appl.* 3: 327-339.

Kennedy, J. S. and Stroyan, H. L. G. 1959. Biology of aphids. *A. Rev. Ent.* 4: 139-160.

Lees, A. D. 1961. Clonal polymorphism in aphids. In *Insect Polymorphism,* Symposium No. 1. Roy. Ent. Soc. London: 68-79.

—— 1966. The control of polymorphism in aphids. In *Adv. Insect Physiol.* 3: 207-277.

—— 1967. Direct and indirect effects of day length on the aphid *Megoura viciae* Buckton. *J. Insect Physiol.* 13: 1781-1785.

Mittler, T. E. 1971. Some effects on the aphid *Myzus persicae* of ingesting antibiotics incorporated into artificial diets. *J. Insect Physiol.* 17: 1333-1347.

Mittler, T. E. and Kleinjan, J. E. 1970. Effect of artificial diet composition on wing-production by the aphid *Myzus persicae. J. Insect. Physiol.* 16: 833-850.

Mittler, T. E. and Sutherland, O. R. W. 1969. Dietary influences on aphid polymorphism. *Entomologia exp. appl.* 12: 703-713.

Pergande, T. 1901. The life history of two species of plant-lice inhabiting both the witch-hazel and birch. *U.S. Dept. Agr. Div. Entomol. Tech. Ser.* 9: 1-44.

Richards, O. W. 1961. An introduction to the study of polymorphism in insects. In *Insect Polymorphism,* Symposium No. 1. Roy. Ent. Soc. London: 1-10.

Schaefers, G. A. 1972. The role of nutrition in alary polymorphism among the Aphididae—an overview. *Search Agr. Entomol.* 2: 1-8.

Shull, A. F. 1938. Time of determination and time of differentiation of aphid wings. *Amer. Nat.* 72: 170-179.

Slingerland, M. V. 1893. Some observations upon plant-lice. *Science* 21: 48-49.

Sutherland, O. R. W. and Mittler, T. E. 1969. Sexual forms of the pea aphid *Acyrthosiphon pisum,* produced on an artificial diet. *Entomologia exp. appl.* 12: 240-241.

White, D. F. 1968. Cabbage aphid: effect of isolation on form and on endocrine activity. *Science* 159: 218-219.

—— 1971. Corpus allatum activity associated with development of wing buds in cabbage aphid embryos and larvae. *J. Insect Physiol.* 17: 761-773.

APHID HOST PLANT RELATIONSHIPS
Some Recent Studies

By H. F. van Emden

Department of Horticulture, The University, Reading, Berkshire, England

Presumably the lure of adequate numbers rather than the challenge of variability lures entomologists to work on aphids (van Emden, 1972a) so that workers on any aspect of aphid biology, including host plant relationships, proliferate rapidly like the objects of their study. A review of the aphid host plant relationship in 1972 must therefore make a previous review its starting point and this paper should be seen as a supplement to the section on host plant relationships in 'The Ecology of *Myzus persicae*' (van Emden, Eastop, Hughes & Way, 1969), though here no special emphasis will be placed on this one species. The same order of subject matter as used in van Emden *et al.* (1969) will be followed here.

The initial attack of plants by aphids

Colour is clearly one of the stimuli influencing host selection by aphids (van Emden *et al.*, 1969). Kring (1969) has used choice chambers with coloured fluorescent lamps to identify colour responses of *Aphis fabae*, a yellow-sensitive species. 'Attraction' fell through the series blue, cool green, pink, green, yellow and red and in general could be related to ultraviolet energy emission. Yellow appeared to inhibit flight activity. Moericke (1969) demonstrated a difference between *A. fabae* and *Hyalopterus pruni* in the degree of saturation of yellow which influenced behaviour. *Phragmites* leaves attracted twice the *H. pruni* which settled on beet and the species selected yellow paints only when these had been 'de-saturated' by mixing with white lead. Moericke considered that this very specific colour behaviour led *H. pruni* to seek host plants avoided by other aphid species.

It has been suggested (van Emden *et al.*, 1969) that the final selection of plants by aphids is favoured by the same characteristics as favour subsequent aphid multiplication. Certainly Brown (1972) found that *Schizaphis graminum* preferentially colonised those cereals which were most suitable for multiplication and Wearing (1972) found *Myzus persicae* alatae selected the plants most suitable for a high reproductive performance in a series of Brussels sprout plants given differing water status. *Brevicoryne brassicae* did so less consistently. Daiber (1971) found no difference in the multiplication of apterous *B. brassicae* on five cabbage cultivars, though the red cultivar was clearly less favoured at the colonisation stage (cf. Radcliffe & Chapman, 1965).

Selection of course entails superfiicial followed by deeper probes of the leaf tissue, during which the aphid is presented with a series of 'take it or leave it' situations, mostly involving chemical stimuli. Several workers (cf. van Emden *et al.*, 1969) have failed to detect fluid uptake with radiotracer during short probes, but McLean & Kinsey (1968) claimed to have done so by measuring induced voltage variations associated with liquid flow through the stylets. This has been resolved by Miles (1968), who pointed out that the simple nerve system of the stylets would inadequately serve a sense of taste. Fluids could be drawn up the food canal and then discharged again without any ingestion, but after contacting more complex receptors as have been described in the dorsal epipharyngeal wall of aphids by Wensler & Filshie (1969). This monitoring and the subsequent behavioural decision to stay or leave produces the pronounced host discrimination characteristic of the aphids, and recently reviewed by Eastop (1973). He has deduced that the first aphids lived on trees; they evolved on an extinct group of gymnosperms and progressed by a series of new host acquisitions. These new hosts were usually specifically or generically related to the original host. Considerable host specificity (commonest at about the sub-generic level) occurs in ninety per cent of aphid species yet spans only about ten per cent of vascular plants. Eastop felt that such high specificity suggests there is an evolutionary advantage to the aphid in concentrating the species on plants where dense colonies can form quickly and soon stimulate production of alatae before parasites and predators destroy the colonies. van Emden & Way (1973) also stressed high host specificity as an aphid rather than a plant adaptation; it would maximise the mixing and dissemination of the population throughout the range of distribution of the species. The high host specificity of aphid species is enhanced by clonal variation. Recent work has distinguished apparently differing host preferences of holocyclic and anholocyclic clones of *M. persicae*. On adjacent crops, Blackman (1971) found a large proportion of holocyclic and anholocyclic (androcyclic) clones respectively on potato and mustard. Holocyclic clones also predominate on potatoes in Maine, but not in New Brunswick (MacGillivray, 1972).

It seems logical at first sight, but is indeed deceptive, to postulate that oligophagous aphids discriminate for secondary substances (taxonomic discrimination) and that polyphagous species discriminate for nutrients (physiological discrimination). Work with artificial diets (reviewed by van Emden, 1972b) suggests that, for example, *Brevicoryne brassicae* selects for sucrose and sinigrin whereas *M. persicae* selects for sucrose, amino acids in the presence of sucrose and against sinigrin. However, the probing aphid is presented with a total chemical picture and phytochemical variation *within* as well as between plant species involves changes in both amino acids and secondary substances (van Emden, 1972b).

Pollard (1971) has demonstrated that *inter*cellular stylet penetration is more common than intracellular penetration when *M. persicae* probes through the epidermis and mesophyll of tulip. This in no way conflicts with a general thesis of chemotactic selection at the various depths of probing, for contact with the cytoplasm occurs even in intercellular penetration due to partial rupture of the cell walls.

Kennedy & Fosbrooke (1973) have recently discussed the sap feeding habit of aphids, including how far aphids control their intake of food. They point to results from artificial diets (Srivastava & Auclair, 1971) which suggests that aphids take up much less liquid than their maximum feeding rate when an artificial diet in rich in phagostimulant properties, unless the viscosity of high sugar concentrations limited uptake in these experiments. The factors limiting uptake will be phagostimulatory compounds, and these may often differ from those which, under any particular circumstances, are limiting for aphid growth. Kennedy & Fosbrooke feel that such limitation of uptake may partly explain why aphids on artificial diets reach only half the size they attain on plants especially as they appear to ingest almost twice as much plant sap as synthetic diet (Mittler, 1970a). Moreover, attempts to pressurise complete diets have resulted in little apparent increase in ingestion.

Kennedy and Fosbrooke also point out that little attention has been paid to the problems of osmoregulation that the aphid may have had to solve. On the one hand they can feed on a source very high in dissolved sugar, on the other they can take up distilled water (Srivastava & Auclair, 1971). van Emden and Cull (unpublished), intrigued by the striking diurnal nutrient cycle in the leaves of plants, were surprised to find that aphids (*A. fabae*) gained live weight equally during equivalent periods of day and night feeding. Aphids feeding at night appeared to excrete less, suggesting that day gain might be of dry weight to a greater extent than night gain. This has proved to be the case. Feeding on dilute sap at night would have two advantages for the aphid. Firstly it might restore an osmotic balance in the insect. In this connection it was noted that honeydew excretion rose rapidly in the latter part of the day. Secondly, feeding at night on a diet of lower phagostimulant content might 'encourage' the aphid to imbibe more 'rich' fluid the next day in spite of any imbalance of nutrients and phagostimulants. The diurnal variation of nutrients in plants could be one reason why aphids may be badly adapted to the constant high nutrient concentrations in artificial diets (cf. Kennedy & Fosbrooke, 1973).

The development of aphid infestations

Kennedy & Fosbrooke (1973) have described phloem sap as a 'veritable widow's cruse of water and pre-digested food at a single feeding site', and more is now known of how aphids act as physiological 'sinks' for plant nutrients drawn from, at least with aggregating aphid species, very distant plant organs (Way & Cammell, 1970). Work in the last three years has gone some way to elucidating the importance to aphids of the individual constituents of this 'widow's cruse'. This is because of continued progress of work with artificial diets, and because correlations of aphid performance with the total pool of soluble nitrogen have been 'played out' with reports of unsatisfactory correlations in, for example, studies on plant tissue age (van Emden & Bashford, 1969, 1971; Harrewijn, 1970).

Mittler, Dadd & Daniels (1970) studied the utilisation by *M. persicae* of different sugars in artificial diets. No other sugar approached sucrose in its phago-stimulant qualities, though a number of other sugars could be utilised almost as efficiently as sucrose. Particularly celloboise, sorbose and lactose appeared to be little or unutilised. Mannose and ribose acted as feeding deterrents. Singh Sidhu & Patton (1970) studied utilisation of nutrients by *Lipaphis erysimi* by comparing the nutrient concentration of aphid honeydew with that of expressed radish sap. They found a decreasing order of utilisation of glucose, pentose sugars, fructose and dextrins.

Work at Reading has attempted to correlate individual amino acids with performance of *M. persicae* and *B. brassicae* on Brussels sprout plants. Several experiments (van Emden & Bashford, 1971; van Emden, 1972b) have led to the following conclusions:

(a) The general correlation between total soluble N levels and aphid performance (van Emden *et al.*, 1969) appears to depend on amides. These are often a very large fraction of the total soluble N and appear to correlate with the performance of both aphid species.

(b) More *M. persicae* than *B. brassicae* variability can be included in regressions of aphid performance on amino acids. Different amino acids correlate with the two species and those which correlate with *M. persicae* show greater variation in concentration than those correlating with *B. brassicae*.

(c) Amino acids which correlate negatively with the aphids seem almost more important than 'favourable' amino acids in regressions predicting aphid performance.

(d) The amino acids which have been implicated are listed in Table 1. It must be stressed that they have been implicated solely by correlation in whole leaf analyses and any direct effect of the compounds has yet to be demonstrated. However, it is worth noting that methionine is an important phagostimulant in artificial diets (Mittler, 1970b). Fluid uptake by *M. periscae* is correlated with methionine concentration between 0 and 40 mg/100 ml diet. Moreover, the aphid shows considerably greater utilisation of methionine than asparagine on diets, which parallels a regression coefficient of methionine in plant leaves 26 times greater for *M. persicae* than that of asparagine. Turner (1971) found that absence of methionine in artificial diets also halted growth of *Aphis gossypii*. Artificial diet work would appear the best approach to the role of individual compounds in determining aphid performance, yet there remains a real problem. The work of Miles (1968) would suggest that some amino acids in the plant (e.g. tyrosine and phenylalanine in Table 1) may effect the aphids through a chemical interaction with other compounds in the plant following wounding. Such amino acids would not be identified as important in plant resistance from artificial diet studies.

TABLE I

Amino acids provisionally correlated with performance of *Brevicoryne brassicae* and *Myzus persicae*—van Emden (1972b).

Species	Positively correlated	Negatively correlated
Brevicoryne brassicae	Amide Threonine Glutamic acid	Phenylalanine Glycine
Myzus persicae	Amide Methionine Leucine	γ-amino butyric acid Tyrosine Proline

It has often been passively assumed that secondary substances, though having an important rôle in host selection, then have little effect on subsequent multiplication. However, as they stimulate or deter feeding they can be expected to effect fluid uptake by the aphid and it can be shown (van Emden & Bashford, 1971; van Emden, 1972b) that their concentration varies in different parts of plants and with the physiological condition of the plant. In comparing the performance of *B. brassicae* and *M. persicae* on two crucifer species (turnip and *Sisymbrium*) each with six physiological 'treatments' (two soil types x three plant ages), van Emden (1972b) was able to account for 75% to 80% of the treatment and species variation by a simple model based on response to amino acids and total allylisothiocyanate (mustard oils). Physiological condition contributed considerably to the variability of allylisothiocyanate concentration. The model used a positive response to mustard oils for *B. brassicae* and a negative response for *M. persicae*.

The symbionts of aphids have been implicated in the nitrogen and sterol economies of the latter (reviewed by van Emden *et al.*, 1969). Some valuable histological information on symbionts has accrued from the detailed work of Hinde (1971a, b). She examined the mycetomes of *B. brassicae*, *M. persicae* and *Macrosiphum rosae* and found a common symbiont type resembling the Rickettsiaceae, possibly only through parallel evolution. In *M. rosae*, however, a second symbiont was found and the two symbiont types were housed in separate mycetomes. The symbionts infect the embryos after blastoderm establishment within the viviparae. The phagocytic haemocytes of the aphid digest the continually degenerating symbionts and Hinde felt that the function of the mycetome might be to protect the symbionts from this 'foreign reaction' of the haemocytes. Forrest & McKnights (1972) have cast doubt on the rôle of symbionts in sterol synthesis under natural, as opposed to artificial diet, conditions. Analysis of tops and expressed sap of radish seedlings showed the presence of six phytosterols of which cholesterol appeared particularly well transported in the phloem.

Genetic variation in plants

van Emden (1972c) has examined whether differences in aphid susceptibility of crop cultivars can be related to the amino acid spectrum, using five Brussels sprout varieties chosen haphazardly from a seedsman's catalogue. One variety (Winter Harvest) gave an amino acid spectrum characteristic of high susceptibility to *B. brassicae*, and has since proved this susceptibility in field and glasshouse trials (van Emden & Dodd, unpublished).

Wyatt (1970) reported differences in field susceptibility to *M. persicae* among glasshouse crysanthemum cultivars. The amino acids of four such cultivars were analysed (van Emden, 1972c). 'Prediction equations' from work on Brussels sprouts accounted for the order of resistance of three of the cultivars. The fourth (Dark Portrait) was virtually immune to *M. persicae*, and Wyatt (1970) had reported that painting the juices of 'Dark Portrait' on the leaves of a susceptible variety transferred this immunity. It is only to be expected that the resistance to aphids of some cultivars should result from deterrent compounds of this kind. Todd, Getahun & Cress (1971) have attributed *S. graminum* resistance in barley cultivars to the toxicity of phenolic and flavonoid compounds and have demonstrated this toxicity to the aphid in artificial diet experiments.

Clear problems with predicting resistance to aphids from chemical analyses of plants are that clones of an aphid species may differ in their host plant relationships and that the resistance may change under different environmental conditions. Lowe (1971) examined the relative susceptibility of two sugar beet lines to three clones of *M. persicae* under several environmental condition. Although absolute performance on the two lines and of the clones varied with environment, the phenomenon that one line was resistant relative to the other remained throughout. Wood (1971) also found the performance of three biotypes of *S. graminum* fairly consistent on nine sorghum selections. Markkula & Roukka (1970), however, were unable to separate ten *Acyrthosiphon pisum* clones into three biotypes on the basis of differing resistance patterns in two pea varieties and red clover. Kishaba, Bohn & Toba (1971) reported that muskmelon lines resistant to south-eastern States biotypes of *Aphis gossypii* were susceptible to the western biotype.

Gibson (1971), studying the resistance of three wild *Solanum* species to potato aphids, found that resistance varied not only with the aphid species, but also with the part of the plant and with the physiological condition of the leaf. Another example of the dependence of resistance on ambient physiological condition is the loss of resistance to *B. brassicae* of forage rape at flowering (Dunn & Kempton, 1969).

Plant water status

Wearing (1972a, b) has examined the effects on *M. persicae* and *B. brassicae* of the interaction of plant water status with leaf age. Wilting the Brussels sprout plants caused alate *B. brassicae* to reject the plants, but *M. persicae* continued to select them, though it then avoided the old leaves and colonised the apex. Apterae of *M. persicae* responded with increased performance to intermittent water stress in old leaves. Under conditions of continuous water stress, however, *B. brassicae* in the apex was more successful than *M. persicae*. The apex is, of course, the last part of the plant to wilt and meanwhile it forms a sink for nutrients from the wilting areas of the plant.

Various chemical treatments to plants

Considerable interest has centred on applying antibiotics to aphids systemically through the plant; possibly this arises from earlier work (reviewed by van Emden *et al.*, 1969) linking aphid symbionts to aphid nutrition. Thus Karl & Müller (1969) found that three antibiotics (particularly oxytetracyclinehydrochloride but also chloramphenicol and reverin) applied to the roots of beans prolonged the development and greatly reduced or destroyed the fertility of apterous *Aphis craccivora, A. fabae, Megoura vicae* and *A. pisum*. Actidione, griseofulvin, nystatin and streptomycin had no harmful effects on the aphids.

Earlier work on the effects of herbicides on aphids (reviewed by van Emden *et al.*, 1969) has shown that 2,4-D can stimulate aphid performance. More recently, Hintz & Schultz (1969) have found a rather similar effect of Banvel D, Barban and MCPA on three species of cereal aphids (*Macrosiphum avenae, S. graminum* and *Rhopalosiphum padi*).

Age of host tissue

It has always been assumed (cf. van Emden *et al.*, 1969) that young and old leaves are particularly favourable for aphids because such leaves are likely to be rich in translocated nutrients, particularly nitrogen. This has been based on analyses of tree sap, but of course there is the real difference between trees and herbaceous plants respectively of 'synchronised' senescence versus the continual transfer of hydrolysed materials from old leaves to the apex. Analyses of old leaves of Brussels sprouts and their petioles (van Emden & Bashford, 1969 and unpublished) suggest that it is unlikely that translocation from senescing leaves in herbaceous plants is sufficiently sudden and slow to allow a build up of soluble nitrogen to occur. However, working with *M. persicae* and *B. brassicae* they found that even *B. brassicae*, which shows a reduced fecundity on old leaves, had a higher fecundity per unit soluble N on such leaves than on the nutritionally 'rich' young leaves. Mustard oil concentration was highest in the young and lowest in the old leaves, so that the normal occupation of these leaves by *B. brassicae* and *M. persicae* may be at least partly related to their different response to mustard oils. It is also possible that a lower 'phagostimulant value' of old leaves results in increased uptake of a more dilute, but perhaps more balanced, medium (cf. Kennedy & Fosbrooke, 1973).

Another possible interacting phenomenon of leaf age selection by aphids has been demonstrated by Gibson (1972), who showed a convincing correlation between the stylet length of aphids and their leaf age distribution on potato. The aphids appeared to do best on larger veins and preferred to feed on the largest vein possible within the limitations of stylet length and depth of parenchyma around the vein. Gibson suggested that food uptake by the aphids may be limited in small veins by a reduction in phloem pressure when the aphid punctures the sieve tube to feed.

Excision of plant parts (e.g. leaf discs) induces senescence without export of nutrients from the leaf. Analyses of discs and attached Brussels sprout leaves (van Emden, in preparation) suggest that amino acid concentration (particularly of amide) in discs can rise dramatically. On discs of 'resistant' plants, the aphids appear to benefit from the increased amide. In 'susceptible' plants, however, amide is already adequate in attached leaves. Discing such plants increases the amino acids which correlate with poor aphid performance, and the aphids do less well on the discs than on attached leaves. There is also reduced methionine in discs, which may explain the particularly reduced performance of *M. persicae* on discs of 'susceptible' plants. It was not possible to reverse or cancel out 'resistance' and 'susceptibility' by discing, through there was a trend towards this, particularly with *B. brassicae*. Thomas & Sorensen (1971) similarly found that the order of resistance of alfalfa cultivars with respect to *Therioaphis trifolii* was maintained in excised material. Schalk, Kindler & Manglitz (1969) did, however, obtain a reversal of susceptible and resistant response in two alfalfa cultivars when presented as whole plants or leaf discs to *T. trifolii*.

Several workers have studied the phenomenon of increasing resistance to aphids as the plant ages. The results seem fairly consistent. Harrewijn (1970) found that fecundity of *M. persicae* on potato increased from four to eight week old plants and van Emden & Bashford (1971) also found an early maximum performance of this aphid and *B. brassicae* on Brussels sprouts at six weeks followed by a progressive fall. El-Ibrashy, El-Ziady & Riad (1972) reported a similarly shaped performance curve for *Rhopalosiphum maidis* on barley: performance peaked at five days and then fell progressively. Daiber (1970a, b), however, has shown increased performance of *B. brassicae*, *Lipaphis pseudobrassicae* and *M. persicae* over an extended period in brassicas from spring to late summer. Both Harrewijn (1970) and van Emden & Bashford (1971) reported poor correlations of total soluble N with aphid performance as affected by plant age, but the latter authors were able to correlate their observations with changes in three amino acids for each aphid species as the plants aged.

The condition of the host plant and aphid population change in the field

An attempt has recently been made (van Emden & Way, 973) to quantify the effect of host plant condition on population change in local populations of aphids.

The International Biological Programme field project on *M. persicae* infesting potatoes has provided data taken before high aphid densities had developed. The results suggest that the poor host status of potato is the most important characteristic reducing population increase rate of *M. persicae*, and that variations in the condition of the potato plants are often as important as natural enemies in determining the trend of the population curve.

The effect on the plant of aphid attack

van Emden (in preparation) has made a fairly detailed study on the effects of *B. brassicae* infestation on the dry matter distribution of Brussels sprout plants. Rather surprisingly, effects of small or large infestations were very similar in the severity of effects caused. Dry and fresh weight of all parts of the plant were reduced by infestation. The most striking reduction was in root dry weight, presumably because dry matter is removed by aphids and by increased respiration of the plant (a saliva effect?) and is therefore not available for storage. Plant height was also reduced, and decreased internode length resulted in some rosetting of the plants. The plants also carried fewer smaller leaves; however, photosynthetic efficiency per unit leaf area and specific leaf area (area per unit leaf dry weight) seemed unaffected. All parts of the plant had a markedly raised moisture content confirming the suggestion (van Emden *et al.*, 1969) that the wilting of aphid-infested plants is ascribable to root reduction rather than to the removal of fluid from the plant by aphids. Aphid infestation induced some amino acid symptoms of senescence—a rise in many amino acids, particularly amide, but a pronounced drop in methionine.

An interesting comparison with this study of a herbaceous plant is the thorough and elegant study by Dixon (1971a) on *Drepanosiphum platanoides* and the growth of sycamore. Dixon also found that aphid infestation reduced leaf area, and in this example there was a correlation between leaf area reduction and size of the aphid infestation. As might be expected, smaller xylem vessels were produced to serve these smaller leaves, but aphid infestation reduced the size of the annual ring by a factor many times greater than could be accounted for by the reduction in leaf area. Dixon suggested that growth-inhibiting elements of aphid saliva were perhaps translocated to affect the cambial activity of the tree. He also showed that aphid infestation could increase the quantity of nitrogen in the leaves at leaf fall; thus the aphid appeared to maintain its food source at a level which allowed a continued high reproductive rate of subsequent generations. Other experimental evidence that aphids 'improve their own food supply' has been obtained at Glasgow in recent years. Dixon & Wratten (1971) showed that *A. fabae* individuals reared on leaves together with a small aphid aggregation gained in size and fecundity when compared with isolated individuals. Forrest (1971) showed that plants galled by *Dysaphis devecta* improved the substrate presumably for themselves but also for *A. fabae*. Honeydew of *A. fabae* feeding on galled plants had increased amino acid content, and *D. devecta* was able to increase the suitability of otherwise rather resistant old or nitrogen deprived plants for *A. fabae*. In a companion paper to the one on *D. platanoides*, Dixon (1971b) reported the effects of *Eucallipterus tiliae* on the growth of lime. Here Dixon noted poor root growth (cf. van Emden on Brussels sprouts, above), but normal growth above ground. Again the infested leaves had an increased nitrogen content. In Dixon's studies on lime, infestation caused a reduction in specific leaf area, i.e. leaves were heavier per unit area.

The decline of the infestation

Work under this heading in the last three years has mainly been concerned with the rôle of aphid nutrition in affecting polymorphism. Most results have come from studies with artificial diets, and this topic is currently reviewed by Mittler (1973). However, mention should be made here of a report by Swenson (1971) that the production of sexuparae in *Eriosoma pyricola* appeared associated with the cessation of shoot growth of the pear tree under a range of favourable environmental and host-tree conditions. Swenson suggested this indicated that the aphid 'uses the tree as a source of seasonal information'.

REFERENCES

Blackman, R. L. 1971. Variation in the photoperiodic response with natural populations of *Myzus persicae*. *Bull. ent. Res.*, 60: 533-546.

Brown, H. D. 1972. The suitability of some crops to infestation by the wheat aphid, *Schizaphis graminum* (Homoptera: Aphididae). *Entomologia exp. appl.*, 15: 128-138.

Daiber, C. C. 1970a. Research note. The influence of the host plant on the biology of cabbage aphids. *Phytophylactica*, 2: 69-70.

———— 1970b. Cabbage aphids in South Africa: the influence of temperature on their biology. *Phytophylactica*, 2: 149-156.

———— 1971. Cabbage aphids in South Africa: their field populations during the year. *Phytophylactica*, 3: 15-28.

Dixon, A. F. G. 1971a. The rôle of aphids in wood formation. I. The effect of the sycamore aphid, *Drepanosiphum platanoides* (Schr.) (Aphididae), on the growth of the sycamore, *Acer pseudoplatanus* (L.). *J. appl. Ecol.*, 8: 165-179.

———— 1971b. The role of aphids in wood formation. II. The effect of the lime aphid, *Eucallipterus tiliae* L. (Aphididae), on the growth of lime, *Tilia* x *vulgaris* Hayne. *J. appl. Ecol.*, 8: 393-399.

Dixon, A. F. G. and Wratten, S. D. 1971. Laboratory studies on aggregation, size and fecundity in the black bean aphid, *Aphis fabae* Scop. *Bull. ent. Res.*, 61: 97-111.

Dunn, J. A. and Kempton, D. P. H. 1969. Resistance of rape *(Brassica napus)* to attack by the cabbage aphid *(Brevicoryne brassicae* L.). *Ann. appl. Biol.*, 64: 203-212.

Eastop, V. F. 1973. Deductions from the present day host plants of aphids and related insects. *In* van Emden, H. F. (ed.), *Insect-Plant relationships:* 157-178. Blackwell, Oxford.

El-Ibrashy, M. T., El-Ziady, S. and Riad, A. A. 1972. Laboratory studies on the biology of the corn leaf aphid, *Rhopalosiphum maidis* (Homoptera: Aphididae). *Entomologia exp. appl.*, 15: 166-174.

van Emden, H. F. (ed.) 1972a. *Aphid technology.* Academic press, London and New York, 344 pp.

———— 1972b. Aphid as phytochemists. *In* Harborne, J. B. (ed.), *Phytochemical ecology:* 25-43. Academic Press, London and New York.

———— 1972c. Plant resistance to insect pests. Developing 'risk-rating' procedures, *S P A N* 15: 71-74.

van Emden, H. F. and Bashford, M. A. 1969. A comparison of the reproduction of *Brevicoryne brassicae* and *Myzus persicae* in relation to soluble nitrogen concentration and leaf age (leaf position) in the Brussels sprout plant. *Entomologia exp. appl.*, 12: 351-364.

———— 1971. The performance of *Brevicoryne brassicae* and *Myzus persicae* in relation to leaf age and leaf amino acids. *Entomologia exp. appl.*, 14: 349-360.

van Emden, H. F., Eastop, V. F., Hughes, R. D. and Way, M. J. (1969). The ecology of *Myzus persicae*. *A. Rev. Ent.*, 14: 197-270.

van Emden, H. F. and Way, M. J. 1973. Host plants in the population dynamics of insects. *In* van Emden, H. F. (ed.), *Insect-Plant relationships:* 181-199. Blackwell, Oxford.

Forrest, J. M. S. 1971. The growth of *Aphis fabae* as an indicator of the nutritional advantage of galling to the apple aphid *Dysaphis devecta*. *Entomologia exp. appl.*, 14: 477-483.

Forrest, J. M. S. and Knights, B. A. 1972. Presence of phytosterols in the food of the aphid, *Myzus persicae*. *J. Insect Physiol.*, 18: 723-728.

Gibson, R. W. 1971. The resistance of three *Solanum* species to *Myzus persicae*, *Macrosiphum euphorbiae and Aulacorthum solani* (Aphididae: Homoptera). *Ann. appl. Biol.*, 68: 245-251.

——— 1972. The distribution of aphids on potato leaves in relation to vein size. *Entomologia exp. appl.*, 15: 213-223.

Harrewijn, P. 1970. Reproduction of the aphid *Myzus persicae* related to mineral nutrition of potato plants. *Entomologia exp. appl.*, 13: 307-319.

Hinde, R. 1971a. The control of the mycetome symbiotes of the aphids *Brevicoryne brassicae*, *Myzus persicae* and *Macrosiphum rosae*. *J. Insect Physiol.*, 17: 1791-1800.

——— 1971b. The fine structure of the mycetome symbiotes of the aphids *Brevicoryne brassicae*, *Myzus persicae* and *Macrosiphum rosae*. *J. Insect Physiol.*, 17: 2035-2050.

Hintz, S. D. and Schulz, J. T. 1969. The effect of selected herbicides on cereal aphids under greenhouse conditions. *Proc. N. cent. Brch ent. Soc. Am.*, 24: 114-117.

Karl, E. and Müller, H. J. 1969. Untersuchungen zum Einfluss von Antibiotika auf Entwicklung, Fertilität und Körpergrösse verschiedener Blattlausarten an Ackerbohne *(Vicia faba* L.). *Arch. Pflschutz*, 5: 251-262.

Kennedy, J. S. and Fosbrooke, I. H. M. 1973. The plant in the life of an aphid. *In* van Emden, H. F. (ed.), *Insect-Plant relationships:* 129-140. Blackwell, Oxford.

Kishaba, A. N., Bohn, G. W. and Toba, H. H. 1971. Resistance to *Aphis gossypii* in muskmelon. *J. econ. Ent.*, 64: 935-937.

Kring, J. B. 1969. Behavioural responses of winged bean aphids to colored fluorescent lamps. *J. econ. Ent.*, 62: 1450-1455.

Lowe, H. J. B. 1971. Alterations of the expression of varietal differences in resistance to aphids under differing environmental conditions. *P A N S*, 17: 253-255.

MacGillivray, M. E. 1972. The sexuality of *Myzus persicae* (Sulzer), the green peach aphid, in New Brunswick (Homoptera: Aphididae). *Can. J. Zool.* 50: 469-471.

Markkula, M. and Roukka, K. 1970. Resistance of plants to the pea aphid *Acyrthosiphon pisum* Harris (Hom.: Aphididae). *Annls agric. fenn.*, 9: 127-132.

McLean, D. L. and Kinsey, M. G. 1968. Probing behaviour of the pea aphid, *Acyrthosiphon pisum*. II. Comparisons of salivation and ingestion in host and non-host leaves. *Ann. ent. Soc. Am.*, 61: 730-739.

Miles, P. W. 1968. Insect secretions in plants. *A. Rev. Phytopath.*, 6: 137-164.

Mittler, T. E. 1970a. Uptake rates of plant sap and synthetic diet by the aphid *Myzus persicae*. *Ann. ent. Soc. Am.*, 63: 1701-1705.

——— 1970b. Effects of dietary amino acids on the feeding rate of the aphid, *Myzus persicae*. *Entomologia exp. appl.*, 13: 432-437.

——— 1973. (This volume) Aphid polymorphism as affected by diet.

Mittler, T. E., Dadd, R. H. and Daniels S. C. Jr., 1970. Utilization of different sugars by the aphid *Myzus persicae*. *J. Insect Physiol.*, 16: 1873-1890.

Moericke, V. 1969. Host plant specific colour behaviour by *Hyalopterus pruni* (Aphididae). *Entomologia exp. appl.*, 12: 524-534.

Pollard, D. G. 1971. Some aspects of plant penetration by *Myzus persicae* (Sulz.) nymphs (Homoptera: Aphididae). *Bull. ent. Res.*, 61: 315-324.

Radcliffe, E. B. and Chapman, R. K. 1965. Seasonal shifts in the relative resistance to insect attack of eight commercial cabbage varieties. *Ann. ent. Soc. Am.*, 58: 82-897.

Schalk, J. M., Kindler, S. D. and Manglitz, G. R. 1969. Temperature and the preference of the spotted alfalfa aphid for resistant and susceptible alfalfa plants. *J. econ. Ent.*, 62: 1000-1003.

Singh Sidhu, H. and Patton, R. C. 1970. Carbohydrates and nitrogenous compounds in the honeydew of the mustard aphid, *Lipaphis erysimi*. *J. Insect Physiol.*, 66: 1339-1348.

Srivastava, P. N. and Auclair, J. L. 1971. Influence of sucrose concentration on diet uptake and performance by the pea aphid, *Acyrthosiphon pisum*. *Ann ent. Soc. Am.*, 64: 739-743.

Swenson, K. G. 1971. Relation of sexupara production in the woolly pear aphid, *Eriosoma pyricola* (Homoptera: Pemphigidae), to tree growth in the field. *Can. Ent.*, 103: 256-260.

Thomas, J. G. and Sorensen, E. L. 1971. Effect of excision duration on spotted alfalfa resistance in alfalfa cuttings. *J. econ. Ent.*, 64: 700-704.

Todd, G. W., Getahun, A. and Cress, D. C. 1971. Resistance in barley to the greenbug, *Schizaphis graminum*. I. Toxicity of phenolic and flavonoid compounds and related substances. *Ann. ent. soc. Am.,* 64: 713-722.

Turner, R. B. 1971. Dietary amino acid requirements of the cotton aphid, *Aphis gossypii:* the sulphur-containing amino acids. *J. Insect Physiol.,* 17: 2451-2456.

Way, M. J. and Cammell, M. 1970. Aggregation behaviour in relation to food utilisation by aphids. In Watson, A. (ed.), *Animal populations in relation to their food resources:* 229-247. Blackwell, Oxford.

Wearing, C. H. 1972a. Responses of *Myzus persicae* and *Brevicoryne brassicae* to leaf age and water stress in Brussels sprout plants. *Entomologia exp. appl.* 15: 61-80.

—— 1972b. Selection of Brussels sprouts of different water status by apterous and alate *Myzus persicae* and *Brevicoryne brassicae* in relation to age of leaves. *Entomologia exp. appl.,* 15: 139-154.

Wensler, R. J. and Filshie, B. K. 1969. Gustatory organs in the food canal of aphids. *J. Morph.,* 129: 473-477.

Wood, E. A. Jr., 1971. Designation and reaction of three biotypes of the greenbug cultured on resistant and susceptible species of sorghum. *J. econ. Ent.,* 64: 183-185.

Wyatt, I. J. 1970. Susceptibility of year-round chrysanthemums to aphids. *Gardeners Chronicle,* 167, (II): 10-12.

APHID POLYMORPHISM AS AFFECTED BY DIET

By T. E. Mittler

Division of Entomology and Parasitology, University of California, Berkeley 94720, U.S.A.

INTRODUCTION

Mittler & Sutherland (1969) reviewed most of the information available at that time on the various influences that the nutrition of aphids may have on the polymorphism of these insects—in particular on their alata-production and alatiform development.

This hitherto neglected aspect of the environment may in certain instances play a more decisive role in morph determination and expression than other well-recognized factors, such as interaction between aphids, temperature and photoperiod. Dietary influences are merely part of a variety of environmental factors that simultaneously and variously act on aphids, and these plant parasites respond to such factors by producing the most appropriate morphs for their survival and for the exploitation of their hosts.

Consideration will be given in this paper to recent studies that show that the diet of aphids can have an appreciable and sometimes dominant effect on aphid polymorphism, be it wing dimorphism or the production of sexual forms. Because of the disparity in the amount of information available in these areas the discussion will deal primarily with the influences of natural and artificial diets on wing production.

The food source

Using an artificial feeding technique described by Mittler & Dadd (1964) and Dadd *et al.* (1967), and synthetic diets based on the formulation of Dadd and Mittler (1966), a number of studies made in Berkeley on a Californian strain of *Myzus persicae* (Mittler & Dadd, 1966; Dadd, 1968; Mittler & Kleinjan, 1970) have shown that the dietary availability of certain amino acids and other nutrients affects the morph of larvae developing on such diets. In most cases dietary deficiencies increased the proportion of apteriform individuals. These responses were contrary to expectation, since in the past aphid development on impoverished plants was thought to promote alata production and alatiform development rather than that of the apteriform morph. Recent findings reviewed by Schaefers (1972), however, indicate that poor nutrition even of plant-fed aphids may also result in aptera production, in conformity with the results obtained with artificial diets. *Drepanosiphon dixoni*, in spite of being crowded, developed slowly into small brachypterous individuals when reared on mature maple leaves, whereas larger and macropterous individuals developed more rapidly on senescent leaves (Dixon, 1972). On severely deteriorated leaf disks, *Chaetosiphon fragaefolii* were smaller and produced fewer alatae than when reared on fresh leaf disks (Schaefers & Judge, 1972). Contrary to the view expressed by White (1972) that production of apterae on deficient diets has no apparent adaptive value, the previously mentioned authors (and Murdie, 1969) drew attention to some ecological advantages for the small, brachypterous or wingless condition for aphids under unfavourable natural conditions.

Group effect and isolation

The studies on *M. persicae* using artificial diets were made with groups of aphids, and results could be interpreted on the basis that different degrees of inter-action between the aphids rather than nutrition were responsible. This objection could to some extent be countered on the grounds that the aphids would have interacted more on deficient diets on which they were restless. Studies on this aphid strain were therefore extended by Sutherland & Mittler (1971) by allowing larvae produced by single mothers to develop in isolation on similar test diets.

Performance of these isolated aphids was different from that of grouped aphids, aptera-production being much higher by the isolated individuals. The proportion of apterae among isolated larvae from isolated mothers, though not 100%, was some 25% higher than among grouped larvae (reared in groups of 25-30) from isolated mothers (Sutherland & Mittler, 1971, Fig. 1). Little difference was observed in the performance of the larvae raised in isolation or in groups of 25 if their mothers had been allowed to interact in groups of 10, a large proportion of the larvae in each case developing into alatae. Daily batches of progeny (1-9 larvae)

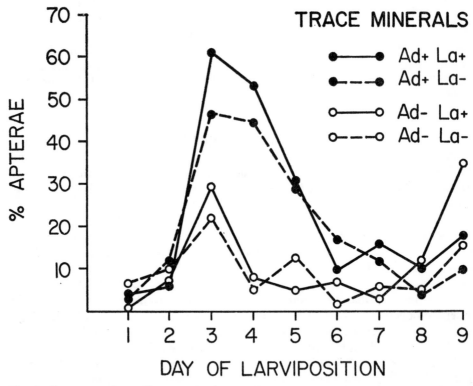

Fig. 1. Percentage of apteriforms to develop on diets with (+) or without (−) trace minerals (Fe, Zn, Mn, and Cu, complexed with sodium EDTA) among groups of larvae deposited by groups of plant-reared apterous *Myzus persicae* on each of 9 days subsequent to being transferred as adults to such diets.

TABLE I

Per cent alata producers among isolated apterous *Myzus persicae* and percentage of alatiforms among their larvae, in relation to the access of the mothers and the larvae to diets of different composition. The larvae were raised in small groups, the size of which depended on the numbers of larvae which each apterous mother produced during one (generally the first) day of larviposition.

Treatments[a] and experimental diets		(No. of adults)	% Alata producers			% Alata progeny		(No. of larvae)
			0%	actual[b] ≥ 50%	diff.[c]	actual	diff.[d]	
Ascorbic acid:								
A	none	(117)	25	47	+24	38.6	+10.4	(892)
B	10% R[e]	(70)	39	23	+18	23.7	+12.2	(501)
C	none	(77)	72	6	0	10.5	+1.3	(557)
9 other vitamins:[f]								
A	none	(125)	13	76	+43	65.8	+37.6	(795)
A	25% R	(96)	20	53	+30	49.9	+21.7	(691)
B	25% R	(58)	5	76	+71	51.7	+40.2	(573)
C	25% R	(64)	6	54	+48	49.9	+40.7	(403)
Proline:[g]								
A	300% R	(106)	15	58	+35	50.9	+22.7	(738)
B	300% R	(77)	31	34	+29	31.7	+20.2	(492)
Standard diet controls:								
A		(178)	29	23		28.2		(1212)
B		(84)	58	5		11.5		(599)
C		(65)	68	6		9.2		(463)

[a] Treaments used:

Code	Mothers on exptl. diets from:	Mothers larviposited on:	Larvae developed on:
A	instar IV	exptl. diet	stand. diet
B	instar I	exptl. diet	exptl. diet
C	instar I	stand diet	stand. diet

[b] % of adults having 0% or ≥ 50% alatae larvae among their individual progenies.

[c] difference between treatment and given control values on standard diet, for the ≥ 50% class values in each treatment.

[d] difference between treatment and given control values on standard diet in the % alatae among all the larvae in each treatment.

[e] R indicates level of component in standard diet routinely used (e.g. ascorbic acid at 100mg/100ml diet).

[f] these diets contained ascorbic acid at the routine level.

[g] these diets contained three times the routine level of proline and half that of glutamine as in tests by Sutherland and Mittler (1971).

of isolated mothers did not contain an appreciably higher proportion of alatiforms than occurred among single larvae from isolated mothers. Hence, in subsequent experiments (Table 1) the performance of such daily batches of larvae rather than of larvae raised in isolation was studied.

Interaction of crowding and diet

Because alata-production by grouped aphids was generally rather high, dietary effects that might have enhanced alata-production beyond that due to crowding were difficult to detect. In some instances, however, the aphids on the standard diet temporarily produced a sufficiently high proportion of apterae despite their crowding, so that some enhancement in alata-production could be observed. Fig. 1 shows this was the case for a diet lacking all the sodium EDTA chelated trace metals (Mittler, unpub. obs.). An indication of a slight enhancement in alata-production as a result of ascorbic acid omission was previously recorded (Mittler & Kleinjan, 1971, Fig. 9) also while using groups of mothers and larvae. However, this difference could express itself more clearly when isolated larvae from single mothers were reared on such an ascorbic acid-free diet (Sutherland & Mittler, 1971, Fig. 3). With groups of mothers and larvae no enhancement in alata-production was detected when the other 9 vitamins were simultaneously omitted from the diet (Mittler & Kleinjan, 1971, Fig. 7).

In contrast, when using small batches of larvae produced by isolated mothers, and variously exposing the aphids during their pre- and/or post-natal development to diets lacking or having only 25% of the routine level of these vitamins, a considerable enhancement in alata-production was evident, as shown in Table I (Sutherland & Mittler, unpub. obs.). This table also shows comparable responses under these circumstances to diets deficient in ascorbic acid or containing higher than the routine level of proline.

Are aphids basically winged?

These and the previously published results clearly show that on certain artificial diets (particularly those highly deficient in essential nutrients) the proportion of apteriforms among aphids raised on them may increase considerably. On other diets the converse may occur. As on plants, aphids are, no doubt, responding to gustatory and nutritional influences that may be antagonistic or reinforcing. As pointed out elsewhere (Mittler & Kleinjan, 1970), a nutritionally deficient diet (e.g. one without ascorbic acid) may be more acceptable to aphids than a nutritionally optimal one, at least as judged from short-term preference tests. Thus more alatiforms on a diet could be an indication of a temporary well being of the aphids rather than a response to a suboptimal supply of a nutrient, particularly if a nutrient such as a vitamin can be conserved by an aphid and passed on to its progeny.

If aphid species producing alatae at some time during their seasonal succession of forms are regarded as 'basically winged', then it seems reasonable to assume that apteriform individuals would develop into alatae were if not for some inhibiting factor.

On adequate artificial diets aphids may develop into alatae, whereas on highly deficient or imbalanced diets such development does not appear to be feasible. Other factors such as isolation can also cause diversion from alata-production, probably by different physiological means. It would seem therefore that when alata-production occurs on artificial diet (and the aphids are not in isolation, or under severe nutritional stress), this does not necessarily indicate a response to suboptimal nutrition. It may be an indication that an adequate diet allows aphids to realise the full potential of their development by production of alatae.

The question may then be asked: Does a similar situation pertain to mature leaves on plants. These are frequently held to promote alatiform development or induce alata-production. Perhaps they should be considered as morph-neutral substrates which permit presumptively alatiform or alata-producing individuals to realise the full potential of their development and become or produce alatae.

It has been customary to consider the problem of wing dimorphism in aphids from the standpoint that various factors cause aphids to produce wings. It might be more instructive, however, to regard the phenomenon from the possibly more realistic point of view which asks 'what causes apterousness in aphids?'. It may then be less surprising to find alate aphids where they generally develop, namely in situations where they are not diverted from an alate to an apterous course of development.

It is noteworthy that in the experiments by Sutherland & Mittler (1971, Fig. 1), 100% aptera-production was not attained on artificial diet, even by isolated larvae from isolated mothers. The small proportion of alatae produced on diet may have resulted from tactile stimulation of the mothers by the few larvae they produced each day, or it could represent another example of the maternal self-stimulation described for a pink strain of the pea aphid (Sutherland, 1969 a).

Either or both of these influences may be invoked to explain similar results obtained by Mittler & Kunkel (1971, Fig. 3), also using the Californian strain of *M. persicae*. Since in these experiments the mothers were maintained singly on diet but the larvae were raised in groups of 25, 100% aptera-production was not expected. A sharp decline in aptera-production to very low levels occurred after the mothers had been on the diet for about a week. In one experiment in which the mothers were maintained for over 2 weeks on the diet, aptera-production progressively increased again in the second week to almost 100%. When the antibiotic aureomycin was incorporated in the diet to derange the biosynthetic functions of the symbiotes of *M. persicae* (Mittler, 1971), results suggested that nutritional deficiencies resulting from long term exposure to sub-optimal diets may be responsible for the increase in apterousness.

Influence of specific procedures

In experiments by Sutherland & Mittler (1971, Fig. 1) using single larvae from isolated mothers, aptera-production on radish seedlings was maintained at 100%, despite the possibility of tactile stimulation of the mothers by the larvae produced (and removed each day). This exclusive aptera-production was not surprising since it had already been shown that a high proportion of larvae, even when raised in groups and derived from grouped mothers, tend to develop into apterae on radish seedlings (Mittler *et al.,* 1970). In further studies on the apterizing effect on presumptive alatiform larvae from radish seedlings, Kunkel & Mittler (1971) showed the morph response to be a function of the time that the larvae had access to the seedlings. This response did not appear to depend on the uptake of phloem sap, since increases in the proportions of apterae occurred among larvae allowed to make successive probes of only 5 minutes, during which time they could not have reached the sieve tubes with their stylets. The effect was greater when the probing of the larvae was interrupted every few minutes during one hour than when the aphids could maintain their stylets uninterruptedly in the cotyledons for one hour. It seems likely that the factor responsible was chemical and that it was ingested. This conclusion is based on the observation that the apterizing effect persisted even when the cotyledons were coverd with a thin parafilm membrane, although the intensity of the apterizing effect was considerably smaller. The factor may, however, be perceived by the nerves terminating at the tip of the mandibles rather than in the pharynx, and since it may pass through a parafilm membrane, the possibility cannot be eliminated that other sense organs on the aphid's body such as on the antennae, tarsi, or labium may also be involved.

Certain lipid and aqueous extracts from the waxy surface of plants as well as volatile components have been analysed and shown by Klingauf and his associates in Germany to effect the probing behaviour of some aphids (*A. pisum, Rhopalosiphum insertum, Aphis pomi*) Klingauf, 1971; Klingauf et al., 1971; Nöcker-Wenzel *et al.*, 1971). Similar efforts could be made to determine the chemical(s) responsible for causing aphid larvae to switch from an alatiform to an apteriform course of development. A reduction observed in the apterizing effect of radish cotyledons immediately after being washed suggests that the apterizing effect may be brought about in part by a water soluble factor, possibly on the leaf surface.

Several other factors have been shown to influence the magnitude of the apterizing effect. Kunkel & Mittler (1971) demonstrated considerable differences in relation to the age and physiological condition of the host, and between different plant species. The greatest response was obtained with radish and nasturtium seedlings, and the least with carrot seedlings. Five other species gave intermediate responses. It may be of significance that the two most effective species both contain mustard oil glucosides—sinigrin in the case of radish, and glucotropaeolin in the case of nasturtium *(Tropaeolum major)*. Mittler & Kleinjan (unpub. obs.) showed that etiolated radish seedlings are less effective than normal green seedlings (Table II).

TABLE II

Proportions of apterae among larvae deposited on diet by groups of apterous *Myzus persicae* and raised in groups on normal green radish seedlings (N), or on diet (D) during the first six days of larval life. Sub-groups, raised on diet, were given access to normal green (N), or to etiolated and yellowing (E), radish seedlings for 6 hours on the day of larval development indicated.

| | Day of development | | | | | % |
	1	2	3	4	5	6	apterae
continuously on N							97.7
	N	D	D	D	D	D	75.7
	D	N	D	D	D	D	61.6
	D	E	D	D	D	D	24.3
	D	D	N	D	D	D	33.0
	D	D	D	N	D	D	20.6
continuously on D							15.7

In order to ascertain postnatal effects on alatiform development in *M. persicae,* Raccah et al. (1971) fed plant reared mothers on a standard diet, and exposed only the larvae to the test diets. When the ratio of sucrose to amino acids was varied, essentially changing the sucrose concentration and maintaining the amino acid level almost constant, the results obtained were the opposite of those recorded by Mittler & Sunderland (1969) and Mittler & Kleinjan (1970), when both mothers and larvae were given such diets. However, in experiments in which the cabbage aphid, *Brevicoryne brassicae,* was raised on diets having different sucrose and amino acid levels, White (1972) obtained results essentially similar to those with the Californian strain of *M. persicae*: the lowest production of apterae occurred on diets almost identical with the standard diet (i.e. the one on which *M. persicae* had performed best).

Raccah *et al.*, (1971) did not observe any effects on alate development when they omitted any of the 10 dietary vitamins including ascorbic acid (cf. Mittler & Kleinjan, 1970; Sutherland & Mittler, unpub. obs.). However, their results using phosphate and magnesium deficient diets support those obtained in the various experiments by Mittler and his colleagues. The authors suggest that differences between the two investigations may be partly a consequence of different experimental designs and partly due to inherent response differences in the aphid lines used. Clearly different clones should be tested simultaneously and under identical circumstances. The value of the genetical approach to the nutrition and polymorphism of insects is emphasised by the studies of Cooke and Sang (1970) and Blackman (1971).

Host-plant condition

Other examples of the manner in which the physiological conditions of the host plant can influence the polymorphism of aphids have been recorded. Dixon and Glen (1971) reported that the bird cherry-oat aphid, *Rhopalosiphum padi*, when reared in isolation for six successive generations on young cherry leaves produced no alatae (emigrants). In contrast alata-production increased from zero to almost 50% from the 3rd to the 6th generation among aphids reared on maturing cherry leaves, and the weights attained by the aphids under these conditions declined progressively in successive generations. This is a well-documented case of poor growth conditions for aphids being associated with alata-production. This should not however necessarily be interpreted as a cause and effect relationship. The growth of an aphid, while being a good index of the nutritional value of the plant (or artificial diet) it feeds on, does not necessarily determine its morph. One may suppose that when young leaves exert an apterizing influence, the aphids would develop into apterae regardless of their absolute growth. However, in nature, the apterizing response has evolved because the resulting neotenous morph can better exploit the good conditions normally associated with young and developing plant tissues by developing faster, and becoming bigger and more fecund than alatae. Mature leaves may neither divert presumptive alatiform individuals to an apteriform course of development nor provide optimal nutrient conditions for rapid growth, development and reproduction; and, hence, small alatae may develop on them.

Forrest (1970) reported that the apple aphid, *Dysaphis devecta*, produced alatiforms, if the aphids were reared on old apple seedlings or on nitrogen-deprived plants which were ceasing growth. In contrast, this aphid and *Aphis farinosa* were reared continuously in the wingless form for over 3 years on young apple seedlings.

Sutherland (1967, 1969 a&b) showed that form-determination was pre-natally controlled in his green and pink strains of the pea aphid, *Acyrthosiphon pisum*, and that alata-production was induced not only in crowded apterous females, but also in isolated mothers fed on mature bean leaves during their larval or adult lives. A mature leaf diet throughout the first instar, even under crowded conditions, did not cause apteriform larvae to switch to an alate course of development (Sutherland, 1969 a). In contrast to the performance of these English strains of *A pisum*, Bonnemaison (1971) found that alata-production in his French strain

71

of *A. pisum* could be enhanced post-natally by as much as 50% if first instar larvae were crowded for 2-3 days on detached bean leaves. This author attributes the increased alata production to a deterioration in the nutrient status of the detached leaves. He discusses the relative amino acid composition of young and mature bean leaves, as well as changes in enzymes and amino acids resulting from the leaves being detached, but unfortunately he provides no comparative data on the growth or reproduction of the aphids on attached and detached leaves.

While there is evidence that physiological changes take place in leaves on being detached (e.g. enzymatic changes recorded by Farkas *et al.,* 1964; build-up of sugar in phloem observed by Leonard & Glenn, 1968), there is no reason to suppose that increased alata-production is a consequence of a deterioration in the nutritional value to the aphids of such leaves. However, in a number of instances detached leaves have been found to be more suitable for rearing aphids than similar, but attached, leaves (MacGillivray, 1954, 1956; Mackinnon, 1961). An extreme instance of this is provided by a bean variety which is relatively resistant to the black bean aphid, *A. fabae,* which Müller (1968) found became highly suitable for the aphid after being detached.

Poor nutrition has also been held to trigger the production of winged emigrants in the damson-hop aphid, *Phorodon humuli,* that migrates from *Prunus* to hops. The effect was shown to be independent of crowding (Kriz, 1966).

With regard to gynopara-production by *Dysaphis plantaginea,* Bonnemaison (1970) maintained that optimal nutritional conditions were provided by tough, old plantain leaves, while young leaves from the same plants increased mortality, reduced fecundity, and reduced the percentage of alatiform morphs produced. It remains to be established, however, whether this is a question of taste or nutrient value, and above all whether there is an actual change in food preference of gynoparae in this species as a result of exposure to short photoperiod, in a manner analogous to the findings of Kennedy & Booth (1954) and Dixon (1971) on *A. fabae* and *Rhopalosiphum padi.* In *A. fabae* nutrient discrimination appears to be more important than flavour discrimination in host selection (Kennedy & Booth, 1951, 1954), but in *Rhopalosiphum padi* the reverse is true (Dixon, 1971). These apparently contradictory situations were reconciled by Dixon (1971) when he pointed out that a response to nutrient status would be of greater value to the highly polyphagous *A. fabae* than to *R. padi* which is restricted in its host range. The fact remains, however, that while *A. fabae* colonizes many different specied of secondary host plants in the summer, it is nevertheless limited to one or two species of primary host plant for overwintering purposes.

Perhaps the emphasis should not be placed on the development of specific flavour discrimination by gynoparae. In *A. fabae,* for example, even the summer forms prefer nutritionally suitable leaves of their winter host to leaves of the summer host plants (Kennedy & Booth, 1951). Instead, the emphasis might better be placed on the increased or wider acceptance by the summer forms of different host plants.

Some 50 years ago, Börner observed that an aphid species produced no sexuals on a very young plant, but did so on a senescent plant under the same experimental conditions. Could this have been because the sexuals or their mothers would not feed and survive on the young plants? It is equally plausible however that the metabolic requirements of the various morphs differ. Hence, we cannot be sure at this stage to what extent the production and performance of the different morphs is a matter of nutrition or a question of taste.

Few studies exist that demonstrate conclusively that the morph of aphids can be affected by the photoperiodic regime to which their host plants (rather than the aphids themselves) are subjected. A recent study by Krieger (1972), though subject to criticism on the possible direct effect of the red light used on the experimental aphid (*Dactynotus ambrosiae*), is however of considerable interest. It points up a valuable approach to this technically difficult field of investigation, namely the use of 'short day plants', such as species of *Xanthium* (the host plant of *D. ambrosiae*), *Chrysanthemum* or *Poinsettia,* as indicators of photoperiod-induced changes in the physiology of the host plant of an aphid.

DISCUSSION

From this review it is evident that the inter-relationships between nutrition and aphid polymorphism are extremely varied, as varied as the many facets of nutrition and the various morphs in which aphids can exist. Differences in food quality (whether of nutrients or non-nutrients) are perceived by the aphid through gustation, and may be interpreted by the aphid's central nervous system to indicate an actual or impending decline or improvement in the condition of a host plant or parts thereof. Because the responses are generally fairly clear cut and the period of determination limited to certain pre- or post-natal stages, a change in the developmental programming appears to be involved. Although differences in the nutrient value of the food and its quantitative availability may also act rapidly enough to affect these developmental switch mechanisms, such differences are more likely to exert themselves by their longer term influences on the metabolism of the insects. In this category one can envisage changes in protein and sterol synthesis affecting the development of wing muscles and associated alary structures, the hormonal balance that is invoked in the development of the various morphs (Lees, 1966; von Dehn, 1969; White, 1972), and the overall growth and development rate of the aphids.

Thus, aphids appear to have evolved the ability to profit from certain environmental cues (e.g. mutual tactile stimulation; photoperiod; properties of different parts or ages of a host plant or of different plant species), and to develop the morphs most suited to successful exploitation. The responses to such cues govern their or their progenies' ability to disperse and colonize other host plants (of the same or a different species) as alatae, or to remain on a particular host as apterae and exploit it if it is suitable, or merely to survive on it if it is not.

These contingent responses of aphids are closely associated with inescapable ones, such as slow or poor growth as a result of low temperature or suboptimal nutrient value and quantity of available food. Our understanding of the phenomenon of aphid polymorphism and its ecological significance will be facilitated when we are able to distinguish further the contingent from the inevitable responses of these insects to their environment.

ACKNOWLEDGEMENT

Grant GB 5398X from the National Science Foundation is gratefully acknowledged.

73

REFERENCES

Blackman, R. L. 1971. Variation in the photoperiodic response within natural populations of *Myzus persicae* (Sulz.). *Bull. Ent. Res.* 60: 533-546.

Bonnemaison, L. 1970. Action de la photopériode sur la production des gynopares ailées de *Dysaphis plantaginea* Pass. *Ann. Zool. Ecol. anim.* 2: 523-554.

—— 1971. Action de la maturité de la plante-hote et de l'effet de groupe sur la production des virginopares ailés chez le puceron du pois *Acyrthosiphon pisum*. *Ann. Soc. ent Fr.* (N.S.) 7: 889-913.

Cooke, J. and Sang, J. H. 1970. Utilisation of sterols by larvae of *Drosophila melanogaster*. *J. Insect Physiol.* 16: 801-812.

Dadd, R. H. 1968. Dietary amino acids and wing determination in the aphid *Myzus persicae*. *Ann. Ent. Soc. Amer.* 61: 1201-1210.

Dadd, R. H., Krieger, D. L. and Mittler, T. E. 1967. Studies on the artificial feeding of the aphid *Myzus persicae* (Sulzer)—IV. Requirements for water soluble vitamins and ascorbic acid. *J. Insect Physiol.* 13: 249-272.

Dixon, A. F. G. 1971. The life-cycle and host preferences of the bird cherry-oat aphid, *Rhopalosiphum padi* L., and their bearing on theories of host alternation in aphids. *Ann. appl. Biol.* 68: 135-147.

—— 1972. Crowding and nutrition in the induction of macropterous alatae in *Drepanosiphum dixoni*. *J. Insect Physiol.* 18: 459-464.

Dixon, A. F. G. and Glen, D. M. 1971. Morph determination in the bird cherry-oat aphid, *Rhopalosiphum padi* L. *Ann. appl. Biol.* 68: 11-21.

Farkas, G. L., Dezsi, L., Howath, M., Kisban, K. and Udvardy, J. 1964. Common pattern of enzymatic changes in detached leaves and tissues attacked by parasites. *Phytopath. Zeit.* 49: 343-354.

Forrest, J. M. S. 1970. The effect of maternal and larval experience on morph determination in *Dysaphis devecta*. *J. Insect Physiol.* 16: 2281-2292.

Kennedy, J. S. and Booth, C. O. 1954. Host alternation in *Aphis fabae* Scop. *Ann. appl. Biol.* 41: 88-106.

Klingauf, F. 1971. Die Wirkung des Glucosids Phlorizin auf das Wirtswahlverhalten von *Rhopalosiphum insertum* (Walk.) und *Aphis pomi* De Geer (Homoptera: Aphididae). *Z. angew. Entom.* 68: 41-55.

Klingauf, F., Nöcker-Wenzel, K. and Klein, W. 1971. Einfluss einiger Wachskomponenten von *Vicia faba* L. auf das Witswahlverhalten von *Acyrthosiphon pisum* (Harris) (Homoptera: Aphididae). *Pflrankh.* 78: 641-648.

Krieger Young, D. L. 1972. Photoperiod and wing production by the aphid *Dactynotus ambrosiae* on the short day plant *Xanthium pensylvaticum*. *Physiol. Zool.* 45: 60-67.

Kriz, J. 1966. Prispevek k poznani pricin prodlouzencho vyvoje msice chmelove (*Phorodon humuli* Schrk.) na primarnich hostitelich a jeho dusledky pro ochranu chmele. *Ochr Rost.* 39: 219-225.

Kunkel, H. and Mittler, T. E. 1971. Einfluss der Ernährung bei Junglarven von *Myzus persicae* (Sulz.) (Aphididae) auf ihre Entwicklung zu Geflügelten oder Ungeflügelten. *Oecologia* 8: 110-134.

Lees, A. D. 1966. The control of polymorphism in aphids. *Adv. Insect Physiol.* 3: 207-277.

Leonard, O. A. and Glenn, R. K. 1968. Translocation of assimilates and phosphate in detached bean leaves. *Plant Physiol.* 43: 1380-1388.

MacGillivray, M. E. 1954. Note on *Myzus certus* (Walker), an aphid new to North America (Homoptera: Aphidae). *Can. Entom.* 86: 190.

—— 1956. Report on potato aphid biology studies at Fredericton, New Brunswick, 1952-1954. *Ent. Div., Can. Dept. Agr.*

MacKinnon, J. P. 1961. Preference of aphids for excised leaves to whole plants. *Can. J. Zool.* 39: 445-447.

Mittler, T. E. 1971. Some effects on the aphid *Myzus persicae* of ingesting antibiotics incorporated into artificial diets. *J. Insect Physiol.* 17: 1333-1347.

Mittler, T. E. and Dadd, R. H. 1964. An improved method of feeding aphids on artificial diets. *Ann. Ent. Soc. Amer.* 57: 139-140.

—— 1966. Food and wing determination in *Myzus persicae* (Homoptera: Aphidae). *Ann Ent. Soc. Amer.* 59: 1162-1166.

Mittler, T. E., Kleinjan, J. E. and Kunkel, H. 1970. Apteriform development induced by radish seedlings in larvae of the aphid *Myzus persicae* reared on artificial diet. *J. Insect Physiol.* 16: 2119-2125.

74

Mittler, T. E. and Kunkel, H. 1971. Wing production by grouped and isolated apterae of the aphid *Myzus persicae* on artificial diet. *Entomologia exp. appl.* 14: 83-92.

Mittler, T. E. and Sutherland, O. R. W. 1969. Dietary influences on aphid polymorphism. *Entomologia exp. appl.* 12: 703-713.

Müller, H. J. 1968. Über die Ursachen der unterschiedlichen Resistenz von *Vicia faba* L. gegenüber der Bohnenblattlaus, *Aphis fabae* Scop. X. Vermehrung und Wachstum verschiedener Aphidenarten auf Rastatter and Schlanstedter Ackerbohnen. *Entomologia exp. appl.* 11: 355-371.

Murdie, G. 1969. The biological consequences of decreased size caused by crowding or rearing temperatures in apterae of the pea aphid, *Acyrthosiphon pisum* Harris. *Trans. R. ent. Soc. Lond.* 121: 443-455.

Nöcker-Wenzel, K., Klein, W. and Klingauf, F. 1971. Beiträge zur ökologischen Chemie 34 Isolierung von Oberflächensubstanzen aus *Vicia faba* L. im Rahmen von Untersuchungen zur Insekt-Witspflanzen-Beziehung. *Tetrahedon Letters* 46: 4409-4412.

Raccah, B., Tahori, A. S. and Applebaum, S. W. 1971. Effect of nutritional factors in synthetic diet on increase of alate forms in *Myzus persicae*. *J. Insect Physiol.* 17: 1385-1390.

Schaefers, G. A. 1972. The role of nutrition in alary polymorphism among the Aphididae— An overview. *Search, Cornell Univ.* 2: 1-8.

Schaefers, G. A. and Judge, F. D. 1972. Relationship between parent size and the production of winged forms in the strawberry aphid, *Chaetosiphon fragaefolii*. *J. Insect Physiol.* 18: 1049-1060.

Sutherland, O. R. W. 1967. Role of host plant in production of winged forms by a green strain of pea aphid *Acyrthosiphon pisum* Harris. *Nature, Lond.* 216: 387-388.

—— 1969a. The role of crowding in the production of winged forms by two strains of the pea aphid, *Acyrthosiphon pisum*. *J. Insect Physiol.* 15: 1385-1410.

—— 1969b. The role of the host plant in the production of winged forms by two strains of the pea aphid, *Acyrthosiphon pisum*. *J. Insect Physiol.* 15: 2179-2201.

Sutherland, O. R. W. and Mittler, T. E. 1971. Influence of diet composition and crowding on wing production by the aphid *Myzus persicae*. *J. Insect Physiol.* 17: 321-328.

von Dehn, M. 1969. Photoperiodisms bei Aphiden. Gegensätzliche Reaktionmechanism bei *Pterocomma jacksoni* Theob. und *Megoura viciae* Bckt. (Homoptera, Rhynchota). *Z. vergl. Physiol.* 63: 392-394.

White, D. 1972. Effect of varying dietary amino acid and sucrose concentrations on production of apterous cabbage aphids. *J. Insect Physiol.* 18: 1241-1248.

75

POPULATION STRUCTURE IN APHID COLONIES

By M. J. Way

Imperial College, University of London, England

INTRODUCTION

Most aphid species depend on ephemeral food supplies and either successively colonise different food plants as they become suitable, or possess diapause-type mechanisms for survival during periods when the chosen host plant is nutritionally inadequate. The frequently 'gypsy' mode of life is accentuated by the seeming hypersensitivity of the aphid to the physiological state of the plant (Kennedy & Stroyan, 1959; van Emden 1973).

Even aphid species which can maintain continuous populations on a single host plant, e.g. *Drepanosiphum platanoidis* (Shrk.) on sycamore, may disperse widely as indicated by trap catches. It therefore seems to be a characteristic of most aphids that their population regulation must depend on interactions that occur within large regions, usually of indefinable area. Such regions may be conceived as ones within which virtually all the time the population is sufficiently self-contained to be insignificantly affected by what happens to the species elsewhere.

Within such regions we can define population groupings of decreasing size and complexity ranging from those occurring on a fairly distinct group of plants, as in a field or wood, to those on a single plant and basically to those in a definitive colony (i.e. aggregate) on a plant. The formation and persistence of such a colony represents true gregariousness (Ibbotson & Kennedy, 1951; Kennedy & Crawley, 1967). The colony may be clearly circumscribed and relatively persistent as with the cabbage aphid, *Brevicoryne brassicae* (L.), or be a loose, usually less persistent aggregate as with *Myzus persicae* (Sulz.) or it may be one which can frequently move and reform on different leaves of the same tree as do groups of the alate adults of *D. platanoidis*.

The aim of this paper is to discuss the qualities of the single colony or aggregate as it matures and ages, and, overall, to consider the selective value or colony formation in relation to the utilisation of local resources and to the dynamics of the regional population.

BASIC ATTRIBUTES OF THE COLONY

The wide variation in type of colony according to aphid species makes it impossible to generalise. The *B. brassicae* colony will be used as a detailed example, with appropriate reference to aphids that exemplify other kinds of colony structure.

Except on young plants, *B. brassicae* forms colonies on the flat surfaces of exposed mature and old leaves (van Emden, 1965) of *Brassica* species such as Brussels Sprouts, *B. oleracea gemmifera,* on which the development of distinct colonies can be followed for weeks or months. A colony is normally established by a closely aggregated group of up to about twenty progeny of an immigrant alate adult. When development from birth of isolated aphids was compared with that of groups of twenty (Way & Cammell, 1970), it was shown that the grouped ones grew larger (mean fore tibial length of adult = 0.530 mm compared with 0.511 mm for aphids reared alone, $p < 0.01$). Furthermore, the initial reproductive rate of adults developing from the grouped larvae increased with increase in size of the group from five to twenty and then declined. This evidence of an optimum initial size of a colony ranging from about eight to twenty according to species has been confirmed for *Aphis fabae* Scop. (Table I) (Way & Banks, 1967; Dixon & Wratten, 1971) and for *Acyrthosiphon pisum* Harris (Murdie, 1969). It is probably an attribute of many aphid species and would appear to be of selective value in accelerating the reproductive rate of the vulnerable, newly established colony. Evidence of the underlying mechanism was obtained by Way & Cammell (1967) for *B. brassicae,* and confirmed by Dixon & Wratten (1971) for *A. fabae.* Isolated *B. brassicae* were confined from birth on part of one of the surfaces of a leaf with the other surface bearing either no aphids or a small aggregate (Fig. 1). The isolated *B. brassicae* reared opposite the aggregate were all relatively larger (averaging 14.7%) and produced larger 1st instar progeny. This showed that the benefit of aggregation was not from mutual tactile stimuli but was presumably because group feeding improved the nutritional status of the plant at the feeding site. Even larger differences were recorded for *A. fabae* (Dixon & Wratten, 1971).

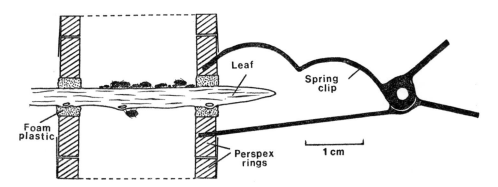

Fig. 1. Section of leaf cage system in which tactile stimuli are excluded as a factor responsible for the beneficial effect of aggregation on development of *B. brassicae.*

Equally striking is the evidence that multiplication rate dramatically decreases as the colony increases beyond a relatively small optimum size—in *B. brassicae* when numbers in the single aggregate rise above about one hundred, although an aggregate may ultimately comprise up to about 10,000 individuals. This was also demonstrated in outdoor field-cage experiments in which the multiplication rate of *A. fabae* was followed on whole plants (Table I).

Hughes (1963) has shown that intra-specific competition may be an important component of 'mortality' in the population dynamics of *B. brassicae.* Way (1968) examined the details of the process in single field aggregates of the same species. Several mechanisms are involved, including the production of an increasing proportion of emigrant alatae and the decreasing size, and hence decreasing inherent fecundity of the apterous adults, but these processes do not begin to operate until

77

TABLE I

Rates of increase of *A. fabae* on field beans, from different sized initial populations (Way 1968).

No. of Original Apterae/Plant	Multiplication Rates Between Days		
	9 - 17	17 - 23	23 - 44
2	x 29*	x 20	x 17
4	x 41*	x 2.	x 6
8	x 46*	x 15	x 3
16	x 36*	x 11	x 2
32	x 27*	x 7	x 2

* All differences significant at p. < 0.05. Other data bulked so not analysed.

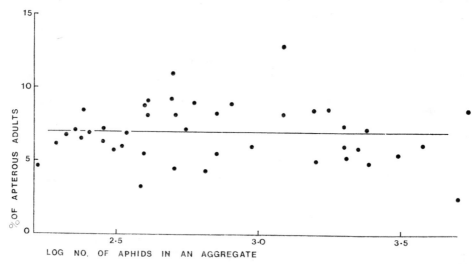

Fig. 2. The percentage of apterous adult *B. brassicae* in colonies varying in size from about 100 to over 5000. (Adapted from Way, 1968).

relatively late in the ageing of the colony. The basic feature is the effect of crowding on reproduction. The adult apterae seem to suffer most from this stress and perhaps also suffer food deprivation compared with the immature forms. Their reproduction is either slowed or stopped. In *B. brassicae,* the change in numbers of progeny is not due to changing proportion of the reproducing forms—the apterous adults (Fig. 2). These remain remarkably consistent at about 7% of the total, irrespective of size (or age) of the colony from about 100 to over 5,000 aphids.

Such results demonstrate that the full potential for reproduction which many aphids possess is realised only for a very short period during multiplication in the aggregate. The basic cause is self-induced crowding and is particularly obvious in species like *B. brassicae.* It means that there is a reserve of reproductive potential to compensate for certain kinds of mortality. For example, the potential is realised when a young colony is partly destroyed by a predator. Surviving individuals disperse and are consequently released from self-induced restraint on reproduction. This however, cannot be said to provide an adequate explanation of the selective value of the aggregation phenomenon (i.e. it does not explain why the aphid does not reproduce at maximum rate). Certain aphids such as the mealy plum aphid, *Hyalopterus pruni* characteristically aggregate densely on the very young leaves of plum trees. Such leaves are a powerful natural 'sink' for nutrients, which might explain why it is valuable for the aphids to concentrate there. Similarly the colony of the elder aphid *Aphis sambuci* forms a dense collar around the very young shoot in spring from which it can presumably remove the rich supply of nutrients rising to the growing shoot. *B. brassicae,* however, characteristically forms colonies on mature leaves, which are usually assumed to be nutritionally inadequate relative to young or senescent growth. A study of the way in which a *B. brassicae* colony on one mature leaf, diverts photosynthate from other leaves on an intact plant shows that it is acting as a powerful artificial 'sink' for nutrients, successfully competing with natural sinks. Such group feeding effects are presumably sufficiently powerful to compensate for the seemingly inadequate supply of nutrients available in the leaf itself. Thus sucrose synthesised in one mature cabbage leaf, given C14 labelled carbon dioxide, is diverted to the aphid-colonised leaf and away from the natural plant sinks. Otherwise, virtually none is translocated to mature leaves (Table II).

TABLE II

Translocation rates of C_{14} labelled sucrose (mg per hr) in uncolonised Brussels Sprouts and in plants with one mature leaf colonised by *B. brassicae.*

	Translocation rate from uncolonised C_{14} labelled leaf	Translocation rate to 'colonised' leaf	Translocation rate to meristem and young leaves
Uncolonised plant	1.16	0.01	0.26
Plant with colonised leaf	3.35 ($\pm$ 0.51)	0.81 ($\pm$ 0.05)	0.19 ($\pm$ 0.04)

A striking feature of the results is that the drain of nutrients by the aphids increased the assimilation rate of the labelled leaf, in one set of plants by about x 6. Some leaves may therefore have a large reserve of photosynthetic potential which is released (at any rate in terms of sucrose production) when the nutrient drain is increased, as by aphid feeding.

Another advantage of aggregation, which stems from the ability of a *B. brassicae* aggregate on one leaf to use resources from elsewhere in the plant is that this method of exploitation is more efficient than if the aphids were dispersed over the host plant. In laboratory experiments (Way & Cammell, 1970) the *B. brassicae* alatae produced by small cabbage plants with just one leaf colonised were compared with ones from plants with the same numbers of initial aphid colonists distributed evenly on all the leaves (Table III).

Insignificantly (p $>$ 0.10) fewer alatae were produced on the one-leaf colonised plants (3089 on single-leaved compared with 3323 on all-leaf colonised plants) but they were larger (difference not significant at p $<$ 0.05). The plants were still alive on single-leaf colonised plants when the aphid population failed, but those with all leaves colonised were killed by the aphids. This was presumably because only one leaf was damaged directly by the aphids, leaving the others mechanically undamaged and their photosynthetic activity unimpaired as an active source of food for both plant and aphids.

TABLE III

Mean weights of alate *B. brassicae* produced on small cabbage plants with either one or all leaves populated by the same initial number of colonists.

| | Mean wts. (mg.) | | Declining Population (38-39 days) | Approx. mean wet wt. biomass of total alatae per plant (mg.) |
	First alatae (22-24 days)	Peak production (31-32 days)		
One leaf colonised	0.260	0.224*	0.196*	620
All leaves colonised	0.262	0.178*	0.134*	587

* Differences significant at p < 0.05.

THE CHANGING STRUCTURE OF THE AGEING COLONY

In aphid species with distinct apterous and alate forms the simple relationship between crowding and alate production has long been established from laboratory studies (Lees, 1966). In nature, however, the mechanism is complex. In *B. brassicae*, for example, the proportion of alatae formed in the colony increases rather than decreases as the individuals in an ageing population become less crowded (Way, 1968). It is now recognised that food quality and/or quantity can influence alate production through their influence on restlessness and hence on alate-producing encounters between aphids in the aggregate. There is some evidence that food can directly affect alate production in some species (Johnson, 1966; Sutherland, 1967) but this seems to be of minor ecological importance. Furthermore, the evidence of work with artificial diets (e.g. Sutherland & Mittler, 1971) must be treated with reserve because of their relative inadequacy. Thus it is known that the remnants of populations of *A. fabae* on dying plants are often apterous 'runts' despite conditions which 'demand' emigration. Similarly the dietary limitations of 'complete' artificial diets can produce apterous rather than alate forms as shown by the work of Mittler & Kleinjan (1970) and Mittler & Sutherland (1970).

One of the most ecologically significant features of alate production is the evidence of qualitative variation among alatae. Thus Shaw (1970, a, b) has shown for *A. fabae* that some alatae remain behaviourally and physiologically apterous and do not emigrate, others reproduce before departing but seemingly make relatively short flights before alighting, while others appear to be long distance migrants. The work of Shaw (1970, a, b) not only shows that responsiveness to long distance migrant-producing stimuli is increased by the extent of crowding in the previous generation (Fig. 3) but also that the proportion of the different kinds of alatae changes as the colony ages. The results imply a sensitive mechanism in some species which disperses colonising individuals to varying distances from the source according to justifiable risk. As already indicated, the population dynamics of most species must depend on interactions occurring regionally, so the potential importance of the varying qualities of the dispersing individuals cannot be overstressed. This further demonstrates the fundamental importance of the happenings in the individual colony.

In earlier studies (Way, 1968) it was shown that some very large alatae are produced very early in the life of a colony of *B. brassicae*; and it was speculated that these alatae were 'high quality' emigrants, well endowed to emigrate long distances compared with the weaker ones produced later. In contrast, present evidence indicates that this could hardly be more incorrect. Many of these large alatae do not fly; the intense crowding in the young colony seemingly 'triggers' alatae formation, but the stimulus needed to induce the 'mood' to fly, possibly deteriorating food or prolonged crowding, is not then present.

DISCUSSION

The tremendous potential for multiplication in many aphid species enables them to react quickly to favourable conditions for reproduction, with the consequent danger of self extermination through over-exploitation of food resources. This is in contrast to many other animals with slow reproductive rates which have a built-in sluggishness of response to favourable conditions. Aphids might therefore be expected to possess well defined self-regulatory or other stabilising mechanisms despite the superficial appearance of instability.

The mechanism for such stabilisation in relation to changing resources depends on processes that take place in the individual colonies, namely self-induced competition that elicits responses such as decreased reproductive rate, increased alate production, quality variation such as change in size of apterae and alatae and variation in the behavioural and physiological characters of the alate individuals that are produced. Futhermore, marked variation in 'migratory' drive of apterae

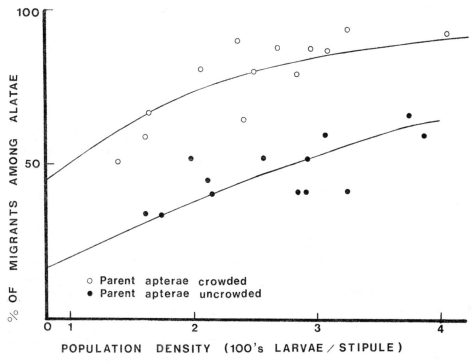

Fig. 3. Effect of crowding the *A. fabae* parent generation on the production of 'migrant'-type alatae amongst their progeny which were themselves subjected to standardised degrees of crowding during development (adapted from Shaw, 1970b).

has been observed in response to crowding, comparable to that which Shaw (1970b) recorded for alatae for *A. fabae*.

Self-regulating mechanisms in aphids therefore may be said to minimise over-exploitation of the plant or, at least, help the aphid to exploit it piecemeal so that production of migrant alatae is optimised on the colonised plant. The extreme hypersensitivity of the alate colonists of some species to food plant quality (Kennedy & Stroyan, 1959) may also be taken as a mechanism for preventing colonisation of some suitable host plants, thereby preserving them or their progeny as food for future generations of the aphid.

In most aphid species, what happens in the colonies cannot in itself be said to be regulatory. Colonies or populations on plants merely possess the mechanisms for exploiting the plant successfully without controlling the upper limit of numbers that occur regionally. The colony therefore acts only by providing an adequate excess of emigrant alatae to top-up and maintain the regional population and we can only speculate on how the upper limit of regional numbers of such species is controlled. Present evidence suggests that in some species, e.g. *A. fabae* (Way, 1967) natural enemies play a major role in such regulation.

We cannot generalise from examples of individual species and it is therefore salutary to examine the nature of the colony structure and its significance in a strikingly different species such as the sycamore aphid, *D. platanoidis*. This species has no apterae and does not necessarily colonise a succession of host plants. It persists on the sycamore tree, spending the summer months as an adult, usually in reproductive diapause. Spaced-out aggregates of the adults have behavioural mechanisms for evading predators (Kennedy & Crawley, 1967) but the striking feature of their colonies is the well defined tendency to form groups on particular leaves. A group may disperse and reform on another leaf. Few of the leaves are colonised at any one time and yet aggregation creates situations where alatae disperse elsewhere despite available food and space on the tree. There is therefore, good evidence that, in this species, self-regulating mechanisms are setting an upper limit to the numbers of aphids which is below the carrying capacity of the tree. Nevertheless, the aphid may cause loss of timber increment (Dixon, 1971), so failure to self regulate numbers at a seemingly low level could seriously jeopardise the condition of the tree for future generations of the aphid. This example well exemplifies the validity of Wynne-Edwards (1962) principles of conventional competition for a token resource—namely 'social' space, rather than for the ultimate resource—food. Again, the colony (aggregate) provides the basic population unit within which such competition operates.

Parthenogenesis, as in aphids, is often considered to have evolutionary limitations, but this needs qualification (Clark, 1973). Assuming that variation can occur, either by mutation (possibilities of which are enhanced by large populations), periodic sexual reproduction or so-called endomeiosis, the prolonged phases of rapid multiplication which parthenogenesis provides offer unusual opportunities for 'group selection' of aphid biotypes in which the attributes of the individual are sublimated to the overall needs of the species population (Wynne-Edwards, 1962). The powerful aggregation phenomen shown by many aphids may be the outcome of this attribute.

The parthenogenetic habit combined with rapid multiplication rate permits very quick selection of biotypes with appropriate characteristics. Most species comprise many different biotypes (Eastop, 1973) and, if they possess strikingly different sensitivities to environmental conditions, for example certain biotypes of *Acyrthosiphon pisum* (Lowe and Taylor, 1964; Sutherland, 1969), those best suited to prevailing conditions can be quickly selected; also, where sexual reproduction occurs, the co-existence of holocyclic, androcyclic and anholocyclic biotypes, as in *Myzus persicae* (Sulz.) provides additional inheritance mechanisms and opportunities for variation within the population that can have an important effect on the ecology and pest status of the species. This is strikingly indicated by the work of Blackman (1971, 1972) on *Myzus persicae* done under I.B.P. auspices. Again, competition within or between aggregates could provide a mechanism for selecting relevant biotypes, as Blackman's work indicates.

There remains an enigma, namely that, despite the plethora of self-regulatory processes which have been described, aphid populations in many countries show violent seasonal fluctuations from very large numbers in early summer to virtual extinction in late summer. No doubt the ability to provide an excess of migrants in the peak period ensures survival, albeit precariously. Yet the growing of crops, rather than benefiting the aphids, is putting some of the species at risk by increasing success in colonisation and by providing conditions for excessive multiplication. This may have at least two undesirable consequencies. First, individual plants may be over-colonised by immigrant alatae or by crawling apterae from adjoining plants (i.e. mortality due to plant species diversity is minimised). The many colonists establish competing colonies on the plant, so upsetting the process of piecemeal exploitation that was described earlier. The outcome can sometimes be observed in crops of untreated field beans attacked by *A. fabae* in Britain. Many very small alatae are produced and many of the aphids fail to mature and die because the host plant collapses. In these conditions about four generations may be required before there is recovery of weakened *A. fabae* to full sized, fully fecund individuals (Dixon & Wratten, 1971). Secondly, natural enemies multiply on the large aphid populations that develop in early summer and later cause severe delayed density dependent mortality (Way, 1967). The relative unsuitability of host plants in late summer adds to this disadvantageous situation. In contrast, before modern agriculture, the natural environment of crop aphids was one of scattered annual plants in relatively small areas of temporarily disturbed land where aphid numbers were probably inadequate to evoke over-compensatory mortality from natural enemies. Such over-compensatory mortality occurs with the lime aphid, *Eucallipterus tiliae* in semi-natural conditions (Dixon, 1971b) but not to the extent of jeopardising the survival of the aphid populations as would seem to be possible with some aphids on annual crops.

REFERENCES

Blackman, R. L. 1971. Variation in the photoperiodic response within natural populations of *Myzus persicae* (Sulz). *Bull ent. Res.* 60: 533-46.
—— 1972. The inheritance of life cycle differences in *Myzus persicae* (Sulzer). *Bull. ent. Res.* 62: 281-94.
Clark, W. C. 1973. The ecological implications of parthenogenesis (This volume).
Dixon, A. F. G. 1971a. The role of intra-specific mechanisms and predation in regulating the numbers of the lime aphid. *Eucallipterus tiliae* L. *Oecologia* 8: 179-93.

Dixon, A. F. G. and Wratten, S. D. (1971). Laboratory studies on aggregation, size and fecundity in the black bean aphid, *Aphis fabae* Scop. *Bull. ent. Res.* 61: 97-111.

Eastop, V. F. 1973. Aphid biotypes (This volume).

Van Emden, H. F. 1965. The effect of uncultivated land on the distribution of cabbage aphid *(Brevicoryne brassicae)* on an adjacent crop. *J. appl. Ecol.* 2: 171-96.

―――― 1973. Aphid host plant relationships (This volume).

Hughes, R. D. 1963. Population dynamics of the cabbage aphid, *Brevicoryne brassicae* L. *J. anim. Ecol.* 32: 393-424.

Ibbotson, A. and Kennedy, J. S. 1951. Aggregation in *Aphis fabae* Scop. I. Aggregation on plants. *Ann. appl. Biol.* 38: 65-78.

Johnson, B. 1966. Wing polymorphism in aphids. III. The influence of the host plant. *Entomologia exp. appl.* 9: 213-22.

Kennedy, J. S. and Crawley, L. 1967. Spaced-out gregariousness in sycamore aphids, *Drepanosiphum platanoidis* (Schrank) (Hemiptera: Callaphididae). *J. anim. Ecol.* 36: 147-70.

Kennedy, J. S. and Stroyan, H. L. G. 1959. Biology of aphids. *A. Rev. Ent.* 4: 139-60.

Lees, A. D. 1966. The control of polymorphism in aphids. *Adv. Insect Physiol.* 3: 207-77.

Lowe, H. J. B. and Taylor, L. R. 1964. Population parameters, wing production and behaviour in red and green *Acyrthosiphon pisum* (Harris) (Homoptera: Aphididae). *Entomologia exp. appl.* 7: 287-95.

Mittler, T. E. and Kleinjan, J. E. 1970. Effect of artificial diet composition on wing-production by the aphid, *Myzus persicae.* *J. Insect Physiol.* 16: 833-50.

Mittler, T. E. and Sutherland, O. R. W. 1970. Dietary influences on aphid polymorphism. *Entomologia exp. appl.* 12: 703-13.

Murdie, G. 1969. Some causes of size variations in the pea aphid *(Acyrthosiphon pisum)* (Harris) (Hemiptera: Aphididae). *Trans. R. ent. Soc. Lond.* 121: 423-42.

Shaw. M. J. P. 1970a. Effects of population density on alienicolae of *Aphis fabae* (Scop.). I. The effect of crowding on the production of alatae in the laboratory. *Ann. appl. Biol.* 65: 197-203.

―――― 1970b. Effects of population density on alienicolae of *Aphis fabae* Scop. II. The effects of crowding on the expression of migratory urge among alatae in the laboratory. *Ann. appl. Biol.* 65: 197-203.

Sutherland, O. R. W. and Mittler, T. E. 1971. Influence of diet composition and crowding on green strain of pea aphid *Acyrthosiphon pisum* (Harris). *Nature* Lond. 216: 287-8.

―――― 1969. The role of crowding in the production of winged forms by two strains of the pea aphid *Acyrthosiphon pisum.* *J. Insect Physiol.* 15: 1385-1410.

Sutherland, O. R. W. and Mittler, T. E. 1971. Influence of diet composition and crowding on wing production by the aphid *Myzus persicae.* *J. Insect Physiol.* 17: 321-8.

Way, M. J. 1967. The nature and causes of animal fluctuations in numbers of *Aphis fabae* Scop. on field beans *(Vicia faba).* *Ann. appl. Biol.* 59: 175-88.

―――― 1968. Intra-specific mechanisms with special reference to aphid populations: In: *Insect Abundance,* edit. T.R.E. Southwood, *Sym. Roy. ent. Soc. Lond.* 18-36.

Way, M. J. and Banks, C. J. 1967. Intra-specific mechanisms in relation to the natural regulation of numbers of *Aphis fabae* Scop. *Ann. appl. Biol.* 59: 189-205.

Way, M. J. and Cammell, M. 1970. Aggregation behaviour in relation to food utilisation by aphids: In *Animal populations in relation to their food resources.* Ed. A Watson. *Sym. no. 10. Brit. ecol. Soc.* 229-47.

Wynne-Edwards, V. C. 1962. *Animal Dispersion in relation to social Behaviour,* Methuen, 653 pp.

84

COMPUTER SIMULATIONS OF APHID POPULATIONS

By R. D. Hughes

Division of Entomology, CSIRO, Canberra, Australia

INTRODUCTION

For more than forty years population theorists have been using mathematical models of animal populations to help them try to understand the numerical changes that were observed in experiments or in the field. Until the last decade the limitations imposed by algebraic solutions meant that the equations used to describe numerical change had to be simplified. This simplication was often carried to the point where the assumptions made in setting up the equations determined the nature of their solutions. Many practical ecologists both past and present have spent a lot of time looking for evidence of population effects whose existence is mere conjecture. The fact that so many influences on the population were ignored also led to such noticeable unrealities that the use of the mathematical models in a predictive way was out of the question.

In some studies of human populations, however, good predictions had been derivable for, perhaps, hundreds of years. The reason for this anomaly was that money was involved. The desire for life insurance, and the opportunity to make money out of it, dictated the need to determine for an individual both his chance of death at present, and his expectation of life in the future, together with the likely increase of population (i.e., of business) over the years. The actuaries did not rely on algebraic solutions to population equations full of assumptions. Their predictions were based solidly on observed death rates in large samples of individuals as similar as possible to the person to be insured. All sorts of influences were considered and their effects calculated, for example, sex, age, weight, religion and so forth. The results of these calculations were set out in, so called, life tables which were applicable for many subsequent years to the population studied. Such tables are still used and are updated regularly to include new influences affecting particular populations.

The life table idea of age specific death and birth rates has been applied to insect and other animal populations for about forty years as a way of describing the numerical changes in a cohort of animals during one generation. These life tables take much more cognizance of birth rates than actuarial tables, and as the observed numbers of individuals are often entered untransformed into the table, it is probably better to call them population budgets (Richards 1961) to differentiate them from actuarial life tables.

The use of such budgets to describe and analyse numerical changes for single generations of insects has little predictive value because the influencs affecting each generation will differ. By observing several generations independently the range of values at each point of the budget can be evaluated, to show the likely limits of the population outcome, but little more can be done. The fact is that the death-rates and birth-rates are not static but are changing all the time.

This point was made more obvious when in 1963 I applied the life table approach to a population of cabbage aphids in which the generations overlapped. Time-specific life tables as they were later called by Southwood (1966), in which the instantaneous death and birth rates of each age group present in the population were calculated on separate occasions throughout the season, showed how much the values changed. Further analysis of the field data allowed some of the relationships of birth and death rates to various seasonal influences to be described.

With the advent of large computers population ecologists were among the first scientists to see the potential for more accurate simulation of biological events. Two approaches were now possible. The first was to make descriptive equations more complex without having to worry too much about their ease of solution. This approach pleased the population theorists particularly but left the field ecologist with many doubts. The second approach was to remake the static population budgets of the field ecologist as dynamic budgets within the computer. Since a system of age-specific death and birth rates is a universally applicable way of describing population events, a computer simulation in which a budget is updated at short time intervals can be as good as the death and birth rate data on which it is based. If a majority of the causal relationships are well modelled the output can be very realistic.

Unfortunately, the iterative procedures involved in such a simulation can be costly in computer time, and so it is usually necessary to minimise the number of variables involved and to maximise the updating interval. Thus, even with this approach, the population ecologist must compromise with reality. Often only the major causal relationships are modelled, the variation caused by the remainder either being ignored (in deterministic models), or incorporated as random variation of the appropriate magnitude (in stochastic models). Without incorporating considerable knowledge of the nature of the variations, experience with including stochastic elements at various places in a model, suggests that population output, after an initial unstable phase, on average eventually approximates that of a deterministic simulation (Gilbert & Hughes 1972).

In the rest of this paper some ways which have been used to increase the realism of simulations of insect populations will be discussed, with especial reference to aphid populations. From this discussion it is hoped that some guidelines can be developed on how a reasonable compromise between practicability and realism can be achieved. Although sometimes favoured by the nature of a life table or budget the admissibility of certain approximations to reality is finally dependent on the projected use of the computer simulation.

REALISM V. SIMPLICITY

(a) *Time-scales*

A population budget usually divides the life cycle of an insect into phases, rather than ages. The reason for this is that the rate of development of an insect is variable, depending always on temperature and perhaps on other factors. Unless it is reasonable to consider that the population lives in a constant environment e.g., an aphid in a tropical rainforest, the simulation must take the changing rates of development into account. This can be done on an absolute time scale— i.e., using the actual age of the insects and modifying the age-to-phase relationship —but it is simpler (and possibly more realistic in sap-feeders, like aphids, in which temperature is the major factor) to develop a physiological time scale of day-degrees above a developmental threshold. This allows age and phase of development to be equated—and the budget to be directly comparable to a population living under natural temperature variations in the field (if the latter can be expressed in day-degrees also). Then, with simulations of single populations, the only apparent difficulty is to estimate all the death and birth rates in the same terms, that is in day-degrees. In other words, a physiological time-scale is used for all phenomena. A further, and sometimes more serious, difficulty may arise if two organisms with different temperature thresholds are simulated in the same model. If the difference is not great and the season of interest is not characterised by prevailing temperatures too near the threshold levels, both species can be modelled using the same physiological time-scale. If such an assumption is inadvisable for any reason—an absolute time-scale, on which the development of each organism in relation to temperature is calculated independently, must be used.

If a physiological time-scale is used, day-degrees tend to be rather numerous, so that a larger unit woud be convenient. The average day-degree duration of the (more-or-less equal) first three aphid instars, which has been called the instar period, can be used as a basis for all rate measurements and has the merit of a clear biological meaning.

Death- and birth-rates can be applied to as many separate life cycle phases as seems appropriate. Separation of the aphid life cycle into phases equivalent to instars is both biologically meaningful and physiologically acceptable. When it comes to the calculations involving the numbers of individuals in each of those phases, the instar period is found to be rather long. Numerical changes caused by the births and deaths of aphids in a colony approximate to continuous functions, and their representation by a single step-wise change leads to difficulties caused by under-representation at the start of a phase and over-representation at its end. So that for the purpose of a basic time scalar on which the computer simulation will run most efficiently, some experimentation may be needed to choose a somewhat smaller unit (e.g., the quarter instar period, or quip, Hughes & Gilbert, 1968).

(b) *Polymorphism*

Simulations of aphid populations are more complex than those for other insects, because of the greater or lesser degree of polymorphism of the individuals involved. No major difficulties seem to arise in handling such polymorphisms within a computer simulation. Our cabbage aphid model was simple in that only two morphs were considered, and the alates were assumed not to reproduce within the colony. Gilbert and Guttiérez (pers comm) have recently completed a model of thimbleberry aphid in which the production of four morphs within the colonies was handled (i.e. wingless and winged parthenogenetic females, males and oviparous females). They also modelled the different properties of the fundatrices in the initial phases of the simulation.

With regard to the multitude of influences that can affect death-rates, morph-determination and birth-rates the important aim is to incorporate into the simulation relationships which give realistic values and natural trends for these rates. Such relationships can always be arrived at by very accurate modelling of the mechanisms involved but unless interest is centred on the particular aspects of that mechanism or its interactions, it is often possible to use a simpler, and not necessarily causal, relationship. An example of this which arose after building the cabbage aphid model was the morph-determination relationship used. Field data suggested that the formation of alates was an effect of increasing density and the relationship was modelled as such. The output closely approximated field observations but an analysis of the model by omission of each variable in turn suggested that alate-formation and subsequent migration was apparently the lowest and most inefficient in a hierarchy of inbuilt density-dependent relationships present. As this conflicted with preconceived ideas of the role of emigration in population control, it was decided to remodel the alate-formation relationship using all available physiological information as to its nature. Bonnemaison's work (1951) suggested that the density-dependent mechanism involved was the chance of interaction between young nymphs and their parents. Although more realistic and perhaps of interest in more detailed studies of the effects of changing the factors upon emigration, the general output obtained could not be distinguished from that of the simpler version. The effects of alate-formation were indeed swamped by the density-dependent mechanisms particularly those acting on the fertility of the adults.

(c) *Distribution*

Another way in which it is possible to arrive at a realistic simulation without the necessity for precise modelling is seen in the effect of distribution of the aphid population between host plants. The relationship of (say) the birth rate to density incorporated in the model is usually determined on single plants in the laboratory. But the output of the model is usually meant to simulate the *average* population changes seen on a large sample of plants. With such a sample the great effect of a few dense aphid infestations on the birth rates of the females within them, will always apparently over-emphasise the decline in birth rate. While it would be possible to simulate this by including the difference in populations on separate plants, it is feasible to model it more simply by applying a conversion factor to the average birthrate. This statistic can be determined by a comparison of model output and observed birth rates in the field.

(d) *Compound relationships*

The major effects of density on the birth rate of the cabbage aphid mentioned above illustrate a case in which an increase in the realism of the model from the first approximation used, proved to be essential. Because adults usually form a tiny proportion of the individuals in a sample of aphids it is difficult to get good estimates of their mortality and fecundity from field data. In the case of the cabbage aphid this was circumvented by obtaining the ratio of first instar nymphs to the estimated number of adults. This ratio shows that 'fertility' declines with population density (Hughes 1963, Clark *et al.*, 1967). Using the relationship so obtained in the initial formulation of the model gave trends in the population shown by the output very different from population trends observed in the field.

The analysis by way of this mechanism in the cabbage aphid, showed that the reduction in apparent fertility with crowding had two components—increased adult mortality as well as reduced fecundity in the surviving females. Observations were reanalysed with this in mind and crude relationships to density of adult mortality and fecundity were incorporated into the simulation with immediate success (Hughes & Gilbert 1968). It did not prove necessary to go on and refine the modelling of the mechanism even more realistically to include the actual effect of density on body size and then the relationship of fecundity to that parameter.

(e) Criteria of realism

This example raises the important point of the need for continuous review of the reality of simulation by comparing its output with field observations. Since a total population trend can be derived from an infinite variety of combinations of birth and death rates it is essential for the computer to give as output a large number of types of observable phenomena which can be compared with field data. Then it is possible to see that not only is the overall population trend similar, but that the side effects of the mechanisms involved also match, e.g., the instar distribution is changing in the same way, and the timing and relative intensity of parasitism peaks are similar, etc.

As it is impossible to estimate the relationships between influences and the properties of insects without error, it is clearly permissible to alter the values of parameters used in the simulation (within the limits of that error) to improve the comparison of computer output with field observations. Again the alteration must, however, improve the simulation of all the recorded features of the population.

(f) Non-generality of approximations

One of the problems arising from the use of non-causal relationships to simplify the construction of a model is that then the simulation is not generally applicable. A valid objection to the cabbage aphid model (Mackauer & van den Bosch, personal communication) is that it does not take the growth of the host plant into much account, only the increase in leaf area being modelled. This objection is particularly important with insects such as aphids which are obligate parasites of their host plants. The cabbage aphid model can be defended as it only purported to simulate the situation where the aphid lives on kale plants in Australia. The pattern of growth in kale is similar from season to season and the probable host plant effects parallel those of aphid density. Thus the observed relationships to density include host plant condition components. The validity of the simulation of cabbage aphid populations on kale is not impaired, but the model gives no insight as to what happens if either the plant growth pattern was altered or the aphid population was initiated later in the plant's life cycle.

(g) Complex models—aphids and plants

There is in fact no difficulty in including host-plant relationships in the simulation. The host plant can be modelled concurrently with the aphid—the amount of detail included depending on the interests of the ecologist. In the cabbage aphid model, leaf area was the only separate parameter defined as this affected aphid densities. In the thimbleberry model, Gilbert and Guttiérez have included the effect of seasonal changes in the host plant as a food source on the fecundity of the aphid. Guttiérez is attempting to relate an index of climatic conditions to the growth of subterranean clover and its associated *Aphis craccivora* populations. Concurrent with the construction of insect population models has been the development of simulations of plant growth. Already attempts to build the effects of insect attack into these models have been encouraging (Wilson, Hughes & Gilbert 1972). There seems to be no reason why simulations of plant growth and of insect populations should not be combined into single computer models. In this way, again any desirable realism of host-plant relationships can be incorporated.

(h) *Complex models—aphids and natural enemies*

The combination of two population simulations is necessary to study effectively the relationships between aphids and their natural enemies. Perhaps the major value of the cabbage aphid model has been for the insight it has given into the predator-prey relationship of *Diaretus rapae* Curtis and *Brevicoryne brassicae (L.)* (Gilbert & Hughes, 1971). This parasite was the only one of the natural enemies observed in Australia for which more-or-less complete biological data was available. This allowed a realistic simulation of its population dynamics to be incorporated in the aphid models with dramatic results. The one-to-one relationship of such parasitoids to aphids lends itself to incorporation in the dynamic budget life table) type of simulation. Furthermore, parasite numbers in the pupal stage can be observed easily (as 'mummies') in the field populations of aphids, allowing comparisons with simulation output which can be used to refine the relationships used in the model.

Attempts were made to simulate some of the effects of the predators and hyperparasites of cabbage aphid—but not enough was known of their biology at that stage to give much insight into their relationships. There is, however, no reason why any natural enemy (if considered interesting or important) cannot be incorporated into a simulation. A pathogen, particularly a fungus disease, would be a very interesting type to incorporate as it would have strong interactions with parasitism.

(i) *Complex models—the future*

The possibilities of combining several population simulations into a single computer model, of e.g., a branched food chain, or perhaps a simple ecosystem, have (as far as I know) yet to be explored, as also has the modelling of more complex relationships of a single species to seasonal changes in its physical environment. But there is no logical reason why these should not be done; time and money are the only limitations. As both these commodities are limited, it is very necessary to have a clear idea of why the simulation of an aphid population is needed.

GUIDELINES

These can be summarised as (1) computer simulations using the dynamic population budget approach seem to be universally applicable to populations of aphids (or of any other sort of animal), (2) because changes in the population structure and number of aphids can only be effected *proximally* by changes in death rates, morph determination, and birth rates, as long as these are allocated realistic values it is not always necessary to simulate the causal relationships. That is to say that non-causal relationships can validly be used to construct a simplified simulation, (3) the minimum amount of biological realism necessary is indicated by a reasonable match between the computer output and the natural population which it purports to simulate. The matching should be observed in as many attributes of the population as can be adequately measured, (4) apart from the need for such matching further biological realism need only be added to explore the relationships of particular interest or importance.

REFERENCES

Bonnemaison, L. 1951. *Contribution a l'étude des facteurs provoquant l'apparition des formes ailées et sexuées chez les Aphidinae.* Doctoral Thesis, University of Paris.

Clark, L. R., Geier, P. W., Hughes, R. D. and Morris, R. F. 1967. *The ecology of insect populations in theory and practice.* Methuen, London.

Gilbert, N. and Hughes, R. D. 1971. A model of an aphid population—three adventures. *J. anim. Ecol.* 40: 525-34.

Hughes, R. D. 1963. Population dynamics of the cabbage aphid, *Brevicoryne brassicae (L.).* *J. anim. Ecol.* 32: 393-424.

Hughes, R. D. and Gilbert, N. 1969. A model of an aphid population—a general statement. *J. anim. Ecol.* 37: 553-63.

Richards, O. W. 1961. The theoretical and practical study of natural insect populations. *A. Rev. Ent.* 6: 147-62.

Southwood, T. R. E. 1966. *Ecological Methods.* Methuen, London.

Wilson, A. G. L., Hughes, R. D. and Gilbert, N. 1972. The response of cotton to pest attack. *Bull. ent. Res.* 61: 405-14.

INSECTS AS VECTORS OF PLANT VIRUSES AND MYCOPLASMA-LIKE ORGANISMS[1]

By K. G. Swenson

Oregon State University, Corvallis, Oregon, U.S.A.

TRANSMISSION OF PATHOGENS

A necessary aspect of plant virus-vector research has been to organize information on transmission phenomena into meaningful categories. This was complicated by the diverse nature of the vectors and has become more complicated by the discovery that a large number of the pathogens aren't viruses at all (Whitcomb & Davis, 1970). They resemble most closely the mycoplasmas of vertebrates but also have strong resemblances to Rickettsiae (Davis & Whitcomb, 1971), and perhaps are not a homogeneous group. They occur mostly among the 'yellows' diseases whose etiologic agents are transmitted by sternorrhynchous Homoptera. Few surprises may be expected among the aphid-borne viruses. Enough of them have been purified to be sure of the virus nature of most.

Two distinct types of transmission are widely recognized. Firstly, there is a type of transmission in which transmitted virus adheres to the mouthparts but in which virus acquisition, retention, and inoculation may be influenced by intrinsic biological characteristics of the vector, virus and host plants (Sylvester, 1954; Swenson, 1963). Such transmission is characterized by virus acquisition in seconds or minutes, immediate transmission, and relatively brief retention (minutes or hours). This type of transmission has been designated nonpersistent (Watson & Roberts, 1939), and stylet-borne (Kennedy *et al.*, 1962). Bradley & Ganong (1953) first demonstrated that one of these viruses, potato virus Y, was carried inside the distal 15 μ of the stylets. Perhaps the most significant recent advance in understanding the mechanism of this transmission is the discovery by scanning electron microscopy that at least one of these viruses is acquired by intracellular probing of the aphid vectors (Hashiba, 1969).

Secondly, a mechanism is indicated whereby ingested virus gets into the coelom, and thence to the salivary glands from which it is ejected into plants in subsequent feeding. Such transmission is characterized by a latent or incubation period in the vector before transmission occurs and by relatively long retention of infectivity (days or weeks). The significance of so-called vector relationships, such as time of retention and changing frequency of transmission with elapsing time, are subject to different interpretations. Unequivocal evidence for this type of transmission includes retention through a molt and transmission following injection of the pathogen into the hemocoel. Such transmission has been designated persistent (Watson and Roberts, 1939) and circulative (Black, 1959). Black distinguishes two types of circulative transmission, propagative (with multiplication) and non-propagative (without multiplication). These may not always be clearly separable, especially if evaluated only on the basis of transmission frequency.

[1] Oregon Agricultural Experiment Station, Technical Paper No. 3392.

These are the two fundamental types of virus transport which are involved in the natural spread of most viruses or mycoplasma-like organisms (MLOs). Anomalous modes of natural transmission occur, including the transmission of regurgitated virus by mandibulate insects (Markham & Smith, 1969) and the transmission of virus on contaminated ovipositors (Costa *et al.*, 1958). Sometimes transmission can be demonstrated in the laboratory which is not important in the field, e.g. tobacco ringspot virus has been transmitted experimentally by grasshoppers and nematodes, but the field vector appears to be thrips (Messieha, 1969).

There are aphid-borne viruses with intermediate transmission characteristics, designated semipersistent by Silvester (1956). Day & Venables (1961) suggest that semi-persistent viruses are simply nonpersistent (stylet-borne) viruses with atypical physical properties, making them more stable and thus retained longer by aphid vectors, and atypical distribution in plant tissues so that the aphid must feed longer to acquire them than to acquire typical stylet-borne viruses. Much has been said of these differences in transmission characteristics but no one has yet proposed a third mechanism by which semipersistent viruses may be transported. There is not, however, agreement on the mechanism of transmission of semipersistent viruses. Pirone (1969) omits them in his review of stylet-borne viruses.

The terms 'nonpersistent', 'semipersistent', and 'persistent' are based primarily on transmission characteristics, such as the readiness with which virus is acquired, presence or absence of a latent period, and retention. They are particularly useful in considering the field spread of aphid-borne viruses (Swenson, 1968). The terms 'stylet-borne' and 'circulative' are used to indicate mechanisms of transmission. Nonpersistent and persistent are not necessarily good terms to designate transmission mechanisms. The stylet-borne myxoma virus persists on mosquito mouthparts for 29 days (Fenner *et al.*, 1952).

Black's (1959) two basic generalizations concerning plant virus transmission by insects are still valid: (1) a virus is transmitted by vectors in only one major insect or arthropod taxon and (2) a virus is transmitted by only one of the basic transmission mechanisms, although transmission by both mechanisms is not uncommon among mosquito-borne viruses (Chamberlain & Sudia, 1961). No evidence has yet developed to indicate that these generalizations do not apply to transmission of MLOs. An attempt to order transmission phenomena might well begin with the insect taxa, especially for entomologists who are accustomed to thinking in these terms. Such a scheme is presented in Table I. An arrangement based on vector taxa is an attempt to organize biological phenomena relating to these taxa; not to classify pathogens or transmission mechanisms. That similar transmission phenomena occur among different vector taxa is hardly surprising since these relationships must evolve within the limits set by vector morphology, physiology, longevity, etc. Similarities in this respect are not necessarily indicative of any true relationships among the pathogens or among the vectors any more than are any other types of evolutionary convergence.

Type of vector and mode of transmission have been associated with fundamental properties of the pathogens in only a limited way. No transmission phenomena have been associated with MLOs that would distinguish their transmission from that of viruses. Serological relationships, type of nucleic acid, and particle morphology are regarded as fundamental bases of virus classification. Viruses having similar vectors and type of transmission sometimes have similar morphology and

Table 1. Occurrence of virus transmission and related phenomena among arthropod taxa.

Taxon	No. Pathogens[1]	Type of Transmission	Examples	References
Mites				
Eriophyidae	At least 8 viruses	Mostly unproved		Oldfield 1970, Slykhuis 1969
Tetranychidae	Report needs confirmation	1 probably noncirculative	Ryegrass mosaic	Oldfield 1970
Beetles and grasshoppers	At least 12 viruses	Noncirculative, regurgitated virus may be transmitted for several days		Gibbs 1969
	Natural spread of some but not all		Turnip yellow mosaic	Markham and Smith 1949
			Tobacco ringspot	Messieha 1969
Thrips	2 viruses	Circulative	Spotted wilt	Sakimura 1962
Hemiptera (Heteroptera)				
Piesmidae	2 viruses	Circulative, propagative	Beet leafcurl	Proeseler 1964
Miridae	1 MLO	Circulative	Paulownia witches' broom	La 1968, Doi et al. 1967
Hemiptera (Homoptera)				
Cercopidae	1 virus	Circulative, probably nonpropagative	Pierce's disease of grape	Severin 1950
Membracidae	1 virus	Circulative, probably nonpropagative	Pseudo curly top	Simons 1962
Cicadellidae	65 or more viruses + MLOs	MLOs[2] all circulative, at least some propagative	Aster yellows	Nielson 1968, Whitcomb & Davis 1970
				Whitcomb & Davis 1970
		Viruses		
		Circulative, propagative	Wound tumor	Black 1959
		Circulative, nonpropagative	Curly top	Ling 1969
		Stylet-borne	Rice tungo	Ling 1969
Psyllidae	3, at least 2 MLOs	Circulative	Pear decline	Hibino et al. 1970
Delphacidae	At least 6 pathogens	MLO, circulative	Rice stripe	Maramorosch et al. 1970

Taxon	No. Pathogens	Type of Transmission	Examples	References
		Virus, circulative, probably propagative	Rice hoja blanca	Jennings and Pineda 1971
Other fulgorids	Several pathogens, mostly MLOs	MLO, circulative	Phormium yellow leaf	Maramorosch et al. 1970
Aphididae	At least 75 viruses	Typical stylet-borne	Potato virus Y	Kennedy et al. 1962, Bradley and Ganong 1953
	At least 12 viruses	Atypical stylet-borne	Cauliflower mosaic	Day and Venables 1961
	At least 30 viruses	Circulative		Kennedy et al. 1962
		Yellows		Watson 1967
		Nonpropagative	Barley yellow dwarf	Paliwal and Sinha 1970
		Propagative	Sow thistle yellow vein mosaic	Peters and Black 1970
Pemphigidae	2 viruses	Mosaics, nonpropagative	Pea enation mosaic	Watson 1967
Adelgidae	1 virus	Typical stylet-borne	Lettuce mosaic	McLean 1962
Aleyrodidae	At least 25 viruses	Unknown	Spruce virosis	Cech et al. 1961
		Circulative; some, if not all, propagative	Cotton leafcurl	Costa 1969
Coccidae (mealybugs only)	At least 5 viruses	Atypical stylet-borne	Cacao swollen-shoot	Kenten and Legg 1971, Posnette and Strickland 1948, Carter 1963

[1] It is difficult to obtain an accurate estimate of the number of pathogens transmitted by some taxa because of the uncertainties of strain relationships. The numbers of pathogens are rough estimates to indicate the importance of taxa and types of transmission for comparative purposes.

[2] Mycoplasma-like organisms.

common antigens, but this is generally restricted to very small groups of viruses (Gibbs, 1969). The same type of vector and mode of transmission may occur among pathogens having diverse particle morphology and no common antigenicity. Brandes & Bercks (1965) devised a classification of sap-transmissible elongate plant viruses on the basis of particle length and serological relationships. Six groups were formed based on particle length. Viruses within each group showed serological relationships which they did not exhibit to viruses in other groups and usually had a common means of transmission. One group consisted entirely of viruses with typical stylet transmission by aphids. Laboratory cultures of viruses in the latter group, such as bean yellow mosaic virus, commonly lose their aphid transmissibility (Swenson et al., 1963) which causes doubts about any fundamental relationship between aphid transmission and virus morphology. Also, other typical stylet-borne viruses have isometirc, i.e., polyhedral, particles.

ENVIRONMENTAL BIOLOGY OF LEAFHOPPERS

Vector work with leafhopper-borne pathogens has been concerned primarily with the fate of the pathogen in the insect, beginning particularly with what transpires during the latent period. Enough pathogens have been shown to multiply in leafhoppers to suggest that most of them do so (Sinha, 1968). It has been possible to show, among other things, the sequential infection of tissues as the viremia develops in the insect. On the other hand, there is no body of knowledge of the experimental biology of leafhoppers comparable to that of aphids. Notable exceptions are the works of H. J. Müller and R. Kisimoto on photoperiodism, diapause, and related phenomena in leafhoppers and delphacids.

From experimental work on diapause in leafhoppers (George & Davidson, 1959; Kamm & Swenson, 1972; Kisimoto, 1959; Müller, 1961; Palmiter et al., 1960; Swenson, 1967, 1971), the different wintering stages of leafhoppers (Müller, 1957), and the fact that diapause phenomena do not closely coincide with taxonomic relationships, we may expect a large part of the wide spectrum of diapause phenomenon known in insects to occur among the Cicadelloidea. In addition to published information on diapause in cicadellids, the univoltine Hordnia circellata winters as adults in reproductive diapause which occurs when the insects are reared under various experimental conditions, including long and short days, (Swenson & Kamm, unpublished data). This may represent a truly obligate diapause, by which is meant that the insect does not have the ability to produce a physiological non-diapause state at this point in its development so that external stimuli are irrelevant.

An unusual situation is represented by the cicadellinid, Draeculacephala crassicornis, in western Oregon (Swenson & Kamm, unpublished data). It winters in the egg stage and is bivoltine at 250 ft elevation. The first generation has no diapause in any stage. The adults of this generation which develop from the nymphs that hatch from the wintering eggs lay eggs which develop uninterruptedly to produce the second generation. The second-generation adults lay the diapausing winter eggs. The growing season is just long enough to produce two generations and most oviposition of the second-generation adults occurs in October. At 500 ft elev., the season is too short for two generations, but more than ample for one. The adults which develop from the wintering eggs mature during the first

96

half of July and are in reproductive diapause. Ovarial development begins about the end of August and oviposition begins in late September. Obviously, there must be intermediate populations in which both univoltine and bivoltine development occurs.

Most of the intensive studies of transmission of pathogens by leafhoppers have involved species that appear to have no diapause, or perhaps the simple provision of long days and greenhouse temperatures, which also promote good plant growth, averts diapause. High temperatures, ca. 21°C or above, tend to offset the effect of short days in diapause induction by speeding up development so that insufficient short-day cycles are experienced (Saunders, 1971). The vector of aster yellows, *Macrosteles fascifrons*, maintained diapause-free development under long or short days at least at 22°C (Swenson & Smith, unpublished data). Thus most transmission studies have involved insects which developed under diapause-free conditions. One wonders if the physiologically different insects resulting from diapause-inducing conditions might show differences as vectors. This could be especially important in the spread of tree diseases where the host plant is in an entirely different physiological state when the different vector generations are active.

Many leafhopper species diapause in the egg stage (Müller, 1957). The biochemical system by which diapause or non-diapause development is induced in the egg is not known. It is not likely to reflect extensive general physiological changes in the female parent. Much more extensive changes would be expected in females going into reproductive diapause where there would be considerable translocation of materials to the fat body in contrast to ovarial development of the non-diapausing individuals. Examples of this sort of diapause in vector species include *Piesma quadrata*, vector of beet leaf curl virus (Krczal & Volk, 1958), and *Psylla pyricola*, vector of pear decline MLO (Oldfield, 1970). The green rice leafhopper, *Nephotettix cincticeps*, vector of rice dwarf virus, diapauses as 4th- and 5th-instar nymphs. Development of the reproductive cells begins early in nymphal development and ceases during diapause. Nasu (1963) commented on an inverse correlation between a tendency to produce diapausing individuals and the ability to transmit rice dwarf virus among geographical races of the green rice leafhopper.

Apart from possible direct or indirect effects of diapause on disease transmission and diapause as an ecological adaptation which synchronizes development with favourable environmental conditions, prevention of diapause is necessary for the continuous development of vector cultures. This is fundamental to many vector studies. There are a surprising number of published reports of failure to culture leafhopper species which indicate that diapause phenomena had not been considered. A further complication is that failure to establish cultures from field collections may occur when diapause has already been determined in the field.

FIELD SPREAD OF APHID-BORNE VIRUSES

Successful interest in vector control by insecticides is exemplified by the long series of papers, relating particularly to beet yellows and potato leaf roll viruses, in the journal, Pflanzenschutz Nachrichten. The disadvantages of present insect control practices represent not so much a need for critical re-evaluation of aphid vector control as they provide an opportunity for new accomplishments. The peculiar entomological problems of controlling virus spread have prevented reliance on single control measures. In addition, some of the predominant means of insecticide control of aphid vectors are what Unterstenhofer (1972) describes as ecologically selective in that they are systemic insecticides applied in the furrow at planting time. The problem in vector control is not so much the disadvantages of the methods presently used to control aphid vectors, although some cases of resistance to insecticides occur, but those problems of virus spread where no control methods of any kind are effective.

Control of the spread of aphid-borne viruses has been pretty much oriented to aphid control in the crop to be protected. Except for viruses introduced in propagating material, primary infections of many viruses, non-persistent, semi-persistent, and persistent, are inrtoduced by migrating aphids from outside the crop. Apterous populations may be responsible for secondary spread of semi-persistent and persistent viruses if not controlled (Ribbands, 1965; Close *et al.,* 1964).

It is generally accepted that most non-persistent transmission in the field is by alatae (Broadbent, 1957). This is illustrated by the fact that no reduction in the spread of potato virus Y occurred when fields were kept free of apterous *Myzus persicae* by applications of nicotine throughout the season (Schepers *et al.,* 1955) and by the fact that non-persistent viruses spread in several crops where there were no colonizing aphids (Swenson, 1968). Sometimes the migration of virus-carrying aphids into a field is so intense that secondary spread becomes unimportant. Seed treatments with systemic insecticides which provided a high degree of aphid control had little effect on the incidence of barley yellow dwarf virus (Harwood & Bruehl, 1961) because of the intensity of primary infections by migrating aphids. In addition, there is good evidence that a substantial amount of secondary spread of semi-persistent and persistent viruses is by alatae produced outside of the planting where virus spread occurs (Broadbent, 1965). There is considerable disagreement about the relative importance of apterous and alate aphids in the spread of semi-persistent and persistent viruses. Opposite conclusions have been reached by different people working with the same virus in the same general area (Ribbands, 1965). Apparently, some important methodological or substantive consideration has been neglected.

A large part of the effort to control aphid-borne viruses might well be preventive and deal with the entire vector species population in the agroecosystem. Such an approach would involve minimizing the effects of aphid populations or depressing their numbers in the agroecosystem, rather than attempting to control them in particular plantings. The area may be prohibitively large, however, because of the transport of aphids in moving air masses, which results in considerable dispersal and mixing of the flying aphids in an area. The relative proportions of different aphid species trapped in areas 60 miles apart in central New York State was remarkably similar, even though the vegetation was different in the immediate vicinity of the traps (Zettler, 1967). Large influxes of migrant *Aphis craccivora* into the central coastal districts of New South Wales originated from pasture legumes and weeds 200-300 miles to the northwest (Johnson, 1967) and the movement of insects and fungi from south to north on the North American Great Plains is a well known phenomenon.

Very little has been done to reduce aphid populations on an area basis. Discussions of biological control tend to discount the possibility of reducing virus spread by biological control of aphids (Hagen & van den Bosch, 1968; Knipling &

Gilmore, 1971). This may result from considering the problem from the stand-point of control in individual fields rather than on an area basis. The papers reviewed by Swenson (1968) showed a relationship between virus spread and aphid numbers in different areas, in different fields, and in different years. Any factor which consistently depresses aphid populations can be expected to have a similar or greater effect on virus spread. Thus the destruction of *M. persicae* oviparae on peach trees by predators was considered directly related to virus spread by aphids in sugar beet and potato in the following year in eastern Washington (Tamaki *et al.*, 1967). Biological control of vectors must be evaluated by its effect on the aphid population of an area over an adequately long period of time, rather than by its short-term effect on the course of infestations in individual plantings.

The effects of aphid populations in virus spread may be minimized in other ways. Many of these involve reducing the extent or availability of virus sources. This is the basis of the use of certified propagating material. E.g., a satisfactory lettuce crop could be produced from seed with 0.3 per cent incidence of lettuce mosaic virus under conditions of aphid activity that might lead to a total loss in a crop planted with 3.0 per cent infected seed (Broadbent *et al.*, 1951). Reduc-tion of *M. persicae* and beet yellows viruses wintering in mangold clamps has effectively reduced yellows incidence in sugar beet in England (Heathcote & Cockbain, 1966) and in Denmark (Heie & Peterson, 1961). Separation of new plantings from infected biennial or perennial plantings may be practical. Spread of the nonpersistent beet mosaic virus was primarily to fields which were within 100 yards of a seed crop (Watson *et al.*, 1953).

Manipulation of planting dates (Hills *et al.*, 1971) and the use of vector-resistant plant varieties may enable susceptible plants to escape virus infection. Freedom from raspberry mosaic in vector-resistant red raspberry is well known (Converse et al., 1970). Wilcoxon & Peterson (1960) suggested that a red clover variety resistant to pea aphid would be a more practical approach to virus control than trying to develop a variety resistant to each of the several red clover viruses that the pea aphid transmits.

The importance of knowledge of vector population dynamics and behaviour can be illustrated by some recent comments of the late F. C. Bawden (1970): 'Forty years on, it is salutary to look back and contemplate the optimistic expecta-tions that knowledge of the nature of viruses would help to control virus diseases. That it has not is vividly illustrated by the fact that tobacco mosaic virus, whose structure and composition is most completely known, is still prevalent in tomato crops in the United Kingdom, whereas little more is known about potato leafroll virus than in 1930, yet it is now a rarity in our potato crops instead of the major cause of loss it was then.' The status of potato leafroll virus reflects recognition of the importance of aphid population dynamics and virus sources and their interrelationships.

REFERENCES

Bawden, F. C. 1970. Musings of an erstwhile plant pathologist. *A. Rev. Phytopathol.* 8: 1-12.
Black, L. M. 1959. Biological cycles of plant viruses in insect vectors. In Burnet, F. M. and Stanley, W. M. (ed.). *The Viruses*, 2: 157-185 Academic Press, New York.
Bradley, R. H. E. and Gangong, R. Y. 1955. Evidence that potato virus Y is carried near the tip of the stylets of the aphid vector *Myzus persicae* (Sulz.). *Can. J. Microbiol.* 1: 775-782.

Brandes, J. and Bercks, J. 1965. Gross morphology and serology as a basis for classification of elongated plant viruses. *Adv. Virus Res.,* 11: 1-24.

Broadbent, L. 1957. Insecticidal control of the spread of plant viruses. *A. Rev. Ent.* 2: 339-354.

———— 1965. The importance of alate aphids in virus spread within crops. *Proc. Intern. Congr. Entomol.,* 12, London, 1964: 523-524.

Broadbent, L., Tinsley, T. W., Budding, W. and Roberts, E. T. 1951. The spread of lettuce mosaic in the field. *Ann. appl. Biol.* 38: 689-706.

Carter, W. 1963. Mealybug wilt of pineapple: a reappraisal. *Ann N.Y. Acad. Sci.* 105: 741-764.

Cech, M., Kralik, O. and Blattny, C. 1961. Rod-shaped particles associated with virosis of spruce. *Phytopathology,* 51: 183-185.

Chamberlain, R. W. and Sudia, W. D. 1961. Mechanism of transmission of viruses by mosquitoes. *A. Rev. Ent.* 6: 371-390.

Close, R., Smith, H. C. and Lowe, A. D. 1964. Cereal virus warning system. *Commonw. Phytopath. News,* 10: 7-8.

Converse, R. H., Stace-Smith, R. and Cadman, C. H. 1970. Raspberry mosaic. pp. 111-119 in N. W. Frazier (ed.), *Virus Diseases of Small Fruits and Grapevines.* Univ. Calif., Berkeley.

Costa, A. S., de Silva, D. M. and Duffus, J. E. 1958. Plant virus transmission by a leaf-miner fly. *Virology,* 5: 145-149.

Costa, A. S. 1969. White flies as virus vectors. Pp. 95-119 in K. Maramorosch (ed.), *Viruses, Vectors and Vegetation,* Inter-science, N.Y.

Davis, R. E. and Whitcomb, R. F. 1970. Mycoplasmas, Rickettsiae, and Chlamydiae: possible relation to yellow diseases and other disorders of plants and insects. *A. Rev. Phytopathol.* 9: 119-154.

Day, M. F. and Venables, D. G. 1961. The transmission of cauliflower mosaic virus by aphids. *Aust. J. biol. Sci.* 14: 187-197.

Doi, Y., Teranaka, M., Yora, K. and Asuyama, H. 1967. Mycoplasma or PLT group-like microorganisms found in the phloem elements of plants infected with mulberry dwarf, potato witches broom, aster yellows, or Paulownia witches broom. *Ann. Phytopath. Soc. Japan,* 33: 259-266.

Fenner, F., Day, M. F. and Woodroofe, G. W. 1952. The mechanism of the transmssion of myxomatosis in the European rabbit *(Oryctolagus cuniculus)* by the mosquito *Aedes aegypti. Aust. J. exp. Biol. med. Sci.* 30: 139-152.

Gibbs, A. 1969. Plant virus classification. *Adv. Virus Res.* 14: 263-328.

George, J. A. and Davidson, T. R. 1959. Notes on life-history and rearing of *Colladonus clitellarius* (Say) (Homoptera: Cicadellidae) *Can. Ent.* 91: 376-9.

Hagen, K. S. and van den Bosch, R. 1968. Impact of pathogens, parasites, and predators on aphids. *A. Rev. Ent.* 13: 325-384.

Harwood, R. F. and Bruehl, F. W. 1961. Seed systemics for control of aphids on oats and barley. *J. econ. Ent.* 54: 883-885.

Hashiba, T. 1969. Studies on the mechanism of aphid transmission of stylet-borne virus. (IV) The insertion site of the stylet related to feeding and probing. *Tohoku J. agr. Res.* 20: 172-187.

Heathcote, G. D. and Cockbain, A. J. 1966. Aphids from mangold clamps and their importance as vectors of beet viruses. *Ann. appl. Biol.* 57: 321-336.

Heie, O. and Peterson, B. 1961. *Investigations of Myzus persicae (Sulz.), Aphis fabae Scop. and virus yellows of beet (Beta virus 4) in Denmark.* Danish Acad. Tech. Sci., 52 p., 16 maps.

Hibino, H., Kaloostian, G. H. and Schneider, H. 1971. Mycoplasma-like bodies in the pear psylla vector of pear decline. *Virology,* 43: 34-40.

Hills, F. J., Lange, W. H. and Kishiyama, J. 1971. Sugar beet yields increased by early planting, yellows-resistant varieties and aphid control. *Calif. Agr.* 25(8): 10-11.

Jennings. P. R. and Pineda, T. A. 1971. The effect of hoja blanca virus on its insect vector. *Phytopathology,* 61: 142-143.

Johnson, B. 1957. Studies on the dispersal by upper winds of *Aphis craccivora* Koch in New South Wales. *Proc. Linn. Soc. N.S.W.,* 82: 191-198.

Kennedy, J. S., Day, M. F. and Eastop, V. F. 1962. *A Conspectus of Aphids as Vectors of Plant Viruses.* Commonw. Inst. Ent. London, 114 p.

Kenten, R. H., and Legg, J. T. 1971 Varietal resistance of cocoa to swollen shoot disease in West Africa. *FAO Plant Protection Bull.,* 10: 1-11.

Kisimoto, R. 1959. Studies on the diapause in the planthoppers and leaf-hoppers (Homoptera). II. Arrest of development in the fourth and fifth larval stage induced by short photoperiod in the green rice leafhopper, *Nephotettix bipunctatus cincticeps* Uhler. *Jap. J. Ent. Zool.* 3: 49-55.

Knipling, E. F. and Gilmore, J. E. 1971. *Population density relationships between hymenopterous parasites and their aphid hosts—a theoretical study.* U.S.D.A. Tech. Bull. 1428: 34 pp.

Krezal, H. and Volk, J. 1956. Über den Einfluss des Lichtes auf die Generations folge der Rubenblattwanaze. *(Piesma quadratum* [Fieb.]). *Nachrbl. Deut. Pflanzenschutzdienst* (Berlin), 8: 145-7.

La, Y. J. 1968. Insect transmission of Paulownia witches-broom disease in Korea. *Korean Observer,* 8: 55-64.

Maramorosch, K., Granados, R. R. and Hirumi, H. 1970. Mycoplasma diseases of plants and insects. *Adv. Virus Res.,* 16: 135-193.

Markham, R. and Smith, K. M. 1949. Studies on the virus of turnip yellow mosaic. *Parasitology,* 39: 330-342.

McLean, D. L. 1962. Transmission of lettuce mosaic virus by a new vector. *Pemphigus bursarius. J. econ. Ent.* 55: 580-583.

Messieha, M. 1969. Transmission of tobacco ringspot virus by thrips. *Phytopathology,* 59: 943-945.

Müller, M. J. 1957. Über die Diapause von *Stenocranus minutus.* Fabr. *Beitr. Ent.* 7: 203-26.

—— 1961. Erster Nachweis einer Eidiapause bef den Jassiden *Euscelis plebejus* Fall. und *Lineoletus brulle* (Homoptera: Auchennorrhyncha). *Z. Ang.* 48: 233-41.

Nasu, S. 1963. Studies on some leafhoppers and planthoppers which transmit virus diseases of rice plant in Japan. *Bull. Kyushu agr. Exp. Sta.,* 8: 153-349 (English summary).

Nielson, M. W. 1968. *The leafhopper vectors of phytopathogenic viruses (Homoptera: Cicadellidae): taxonomy, biology, and virus transmission.* U.S.D.A. Tech. Bull. 1362: 386 p.

Oldfield, G. N. 1970. Diapause and polymorphism in California populations of *Psylla pyricola* (Homoptera: Psyllidae). *Ann. ent. Soc. Amer.,* 63: 180-184.

—— 1970. Mite transmission of plant viruses. *A. Rev. Ent.* 15: 343-380.

Paliwal, Y. C. and Sinha, R. C. 1970. On the mechanism of persistence and distribution of barley yellow dwarf virus in an aphid vector. *Virology,* 42: 668-680.

Palmiter, D. H., Coxeter, W. J. and Adams, J. A. 1960. Seasonal history and rearing of *Scaphytopius acutus* (Say) (Homoptera: Cicadellidae). *Ann. ent. Soc. Amer.* 53: 843-6.

Pstrone, T. P. 1969. Mechanism of transmission of stylet-borne viruses. Pp. 199-210 in K. Maramorosch (ed.), *Viruses, Vectors and Vegetation,* Inter-science, New York.

Posnette, A. F. and Strickland, A. H. 1948. Virus diseases of cacoa in West Africa. III. Technique of insect transmission. *Ann. appl. Biol.* 35: 53-63.

Proeseler, G. 1964. Der Nachweis der Vermehrung des Rubenkrauselkrankheits—Virus in *Piesma quadrata* (Fieb.) mit Hilfe der Injektionstechnik. *Naturwissenschaften,* 51: 150-151.

Ribbands, C. R. 1965. The significance of apterous aphids in the spread of viruses within agricultural crops. *Proc. Intern. Congr. Entomol., 12,* London, 1964: 525-526.

Sakimura, K. 1962. The present status of thrips-borne viruses. Pp. 33-40 in K. Maramorosch (ed.), *Biological Transmission of Disease Agents,* Academic Press, New York.

Saunders, D. S. 1971. The temperature-compensated photoperiodic clock 'programming' development and pupal diapause in the flesh fly, *Sarcophaga argyrostoma. J. Insect Physiol.* 17: 801-12.

Schepers, A., Reestman, A. J. and Hille Ris Lambers, D. 1955. Some experiments with Systox. *Proc. Conf. Potato Virus Disease, znd, Lisse-Wageningen,* 1954: 75-83.

Severin, H. P. P. 1950. Spittle-insect vectors of Pierce's disease virus. II. Life history and virus transmission. *Hilgardia,* 19: 357-382.

Simons, J. N. 1962. The pseudo-curly top disease in South Florida. *J. econ. Ent.* 55: 358-363.

Slykhuis, J. T. 1969. Mites as vectors of plant viruses. Pp. 121-141 in K. Maramorosch (ed.), *Viruses, Vectors and Vegetation,* Interscience, New York.

Swenson, K. G. 1963. Effects of insects and virus host plants on transmission of viruses by insects. *Ann. N.Y. Acad. Sci.* 105: 730-740.

—— 1967. Plant virus transmission by insects. Pp. 267-307 in K. Maramorosch and H. Koprowski (eds.), *Methods in Virology, Vol. I,* Academic Press, New York.

—— 1968. Role of aphids in the ecology of plant viruses. *A. Rev. Phytopathol.* 6: 351-374.

—— 1971. Environmental biology of the leafhopper *Scaphytopius delongi. Ann. ent. Soc. Amer.* 64: 809-12.

Swenson, K. G., Sohi, S. S. and Welton, R. E. 1954. Loss of transmissibility by aphids of bean yellow mosaic virus. *Ann. ent. Soc. Amer.* 57: 378-382.

Sylvester, E. S. 1954. Aphid transmission of nonpersistent plant viruses with special reference to *Brassica nigra* virus. *Hilgardia,* 23: 53-98.

———— 1956. Beet yellows transmission by the green peach aphid. *J. econ. Ent.* 49: 789-800.

Tamaki, G., Landis, B. J. and Weeks, R. E. 1967. Autumn population of green peach aphid on peach trees and the role of syrphid flies in their control. *J. econ. Ent.* 60: 433-436.

Unterstenhofer, G. 1970. Integrated pest control from the aspect of industrial research on crop protection chemicals. *Pflanzenschutz Nachrichten,* 23: 264-272.

Watson, M. A. 1967. Epidemiology of aphid-transmitted plant-virus diseases. *Outlook Agr.* 5: 155-166.

Watson, M. A., Hull, R., Blencowe, J. W. and Hamlyn, B. M. 1951. The spread of beet yellows and beet mosaic viruses in the sugar beet root crop. I. Field observations in the virus diseases of sugar beet and their vectors *Myzus persicae* (Sulz) and *Aphis fabae* Koch. *Ann. appl. Biol.* 38: 743-64.

Watson, M. A. and Roberts, F. M. 1939. A comparative study of the transmission of *Hyoscyamus* virus 3, potato virus Y and cucumber virus 1 by the vectors *Myzus persicae* (Sulz.) *M. circumflexus* (Buckton) *and Macrosiphum gei* (Koch). *Proc. Roy Soc. London. Series B* 127:543-576.

Whitcomb, R. F. and Davis, R. E. 1970. Mycoplasma and phytarboviruses as plant pathogens persistently transmitted by insects. *A. Rev. Ent.* 15: 405-464.

Wilcoxon, R. D. and Peterson, A. G. 1960. Resistance of Dollard red clover to the pea aprid, *Hacrosiphum pisi. J. econ. Ent.* 53: 863-65.

Zettler, R. M. 1967. Winged aphids caught in traps in bean fields in central New York. *J. econ. Ent.* 60: 1320-1323.

THE ECOLOGICAL IMPLICATIONS OF PARTHENOGENESIS

By W. C. Clark

Zoology Department, University of Canterbury, Christchurch, New Zealand

INTRODUCTION

In recent years there have been many studies of parthenogenesis, much of the interest apparently stimulated by the reviews of White (1948, 1954, 1971) and Suomalainen (1950, 1962). Many studies have been concerned with detailed cytogenetic observations aimed at demonstrating the fact of parthenogenesis in a particular species, or at elucidating details of specific mechanisms. Apart from papers of this type there have been some which provided surveys of the occurrence of parthenogenesis in limited groups (e.g. Smith, 1971 beetles; Mockford, 1971 Psocoptera; Olliver, 1971 mites; Nur, 1971 coccids).

The role of sexuality (fusion of gamete nuclei) in evolution, and its absence in parthenogenesis, have been discussed by many authors who have almost invariably come to the conclusion that the benefits of sexuality are so overwhelming, that only perversity can account for the frequency with which parthenogenesis is observed in nature. Earlier writers (e.g. Darlington 1937, White 1948 and Suomalainen 1950) suggested that the genetic consequences of parthenogenesis are either complete heterozygosity or complete homozygosity.

More recent studies are more ambiguous. Carson (1967) showed that ameiotic parthenogenesis can maintain heterozygosity. Asher (1970) showed that in parthenogenetic diploid populations at least three mechanisms are available to maintain heterozygosity. In a later paper Asher & Nace (1971) were able to demonstrate that neither of the predicted consequences (total homozygosity or heterozygosity) was inevitable.

On the utility of sex Bodmer (1970) concluded that sexuality was most important in small populations. Maynard Smith (1971) concluded that except where hybrids between two populations had a marked selective advantage, new combinations of genes would be most rapidly established in populations which eschewed sexuality, except where the breeding population was larger than a million individuals! Eshel & Feldman (1970) came to somewhat different conclusions, but were most impressed by the capacity of parthenogenesis to establish and to increase the frequency of new mutant genetic types.

The study of male haploidy, its possible origin, and evolutionary consequences has been undertaken by Hartl (1971); and Hartl & Brown (1970). Male haploidy is a consequence either of the absence of a fertilizing sperm, as in most Hymenoptera and monogonont rotifers or from pseudogamous development as in some diaspidine scale insects (Brown & Bennett, 1957).

For practical purposes the means of reproduction employed by the Metazoa may be classified as in figure 1. *Regenerative reproduction* is the name I have given to the many reproductive phenomena often called 'vegetative' or 'asexual'.

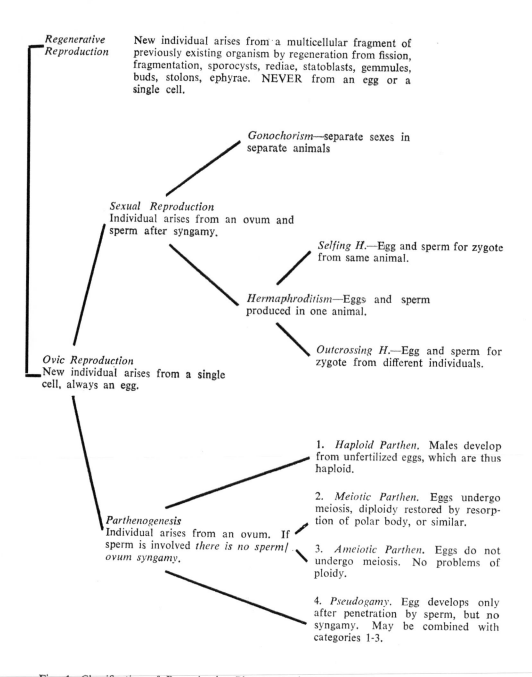

Fig. 1 Classification of Reproductive Phenomena in Metazoa.

This is an attempt to draw attention to the fact that in these instances the new individual arises from a muticellular fragment of a previously existing individual by processes more akin to regeneration than to normal embryogenesis. Such a term also serves to avoid the wholly unsatisfactory grouping of budding and parthenogenesis in a single category of 'vegetative' or 'asexual' reproduction. *Ovic reproduction* (from ovum=an egg) is the term coined for the contrasting condition where the primordium of the new individual is a single cell or egg. In theory this may sound a circular definition, but in practice it presents few difficulties.

The classification makes it clear that parthenogenesis is not a single phenomenon, but a collection of phenomena sharing the common feature of embryogenesis without fusion of gamete nuclei. A spermatozoon or some other body [a fungus (Stolk 1958), microsporidia (Bulnheim & Vavra 1968, Bulnheim 1968) or virus particles (Olsen & Buss 1967)] may be needed to activate the egg as in pseudogamy, but in such cases there is no fusion of gamete or other nuclei. Parthenogenesis may be classified according to other criteria such as the sex of the offspring, or on the regularity of the process—obligate, facultative, cyclical or accidental.

THE OCCURRENCE OF PARTHENOGENESIS

Valuable insights into the role of parthenogenesis as a reproductive stratagem may be gained from a study of the distribution of the phenomenon both ecologically and taxonomically. Such a study is most likely to be informative if we examine particularly the groups in which parthenogenesis is either especially common, or even the only means of increasing numbers.

Distribution of Habitat

When examined in relation to the habitat of the animal concerned, the most striking generalization is the absence of parthenogenesis from marine habitats. The only record of natural (i.e. not experimentally induced) parthenogenesis of a marine organism known to the present author is that of Mesnil & Caullery (1898) in the sedentary polychaete *Dodecaceria concharum*. This species needs reinvestigation.

The absence of parthenogenesis from the sea may be related to several factors. An attractive argument is that the sea provides the most generally stable environmental conditions of all the great habitats, and as we shall see later, parthenogenesis is not normally associated with stable, permanent habitats. Further, for many marine invertebrates (almost all except the Brachiopoda, Mollusca, and Arthropoda) a variety of methods of regenerative reproduction (e.g. budding, fragmentation and fission) are available as means of increasing numbers without breaking up the successful genotype by sexual recombination (by gametogenesis).

In freshwaters, especially temporary ponds, and in salt lakes, parthenogenesis is very common amongst the Crustacea, but is also known in insect groups such as the Simuliidae, Chironomidae, Trichoptera and Ephemeroptera and in a few Mollusca and oligochaetes.

It appears to be generally true that the inhabitants of permanent stable freshwater habitats show less parthenogenesis than the inhabitants of extremely unstable, fluctuating or temporary habitats.

On land and in the soil a situation similar to that found in fresh waters obtains: the inhabitants of permanent habitats show little parthenogenesis, whilst the inhabitants of temporary or unstable fluctuating habitats or more precisely, those which are discontinuous in space and time, show much parthenogenetic reproduction. (Examples of such ephemeral, fluctuating habitats include some moss clumps, dung, decaying fruits, twigs, corpses and indeed any aggregations of rotting organic matter, but they may also include habitats in very high latitudes (Downes, 1965)).

105

Distribution by Taxa

A group-by-group examination of the occurrence of parthenogenesis, such as that conducted by Vandel (1931a) and Suomalainen (1950), indicates that either experimental or natural parthenogenesis is known from at least one example of almost all groups of animals except the Odonata and Mammalia. Thus the known distribution of parthenogenesis on a strictly taxonomic basis adds little to our understanding. Many examples of parthenogenesis are probably best regarded as unimportant aberrations of a normal gonochoristic system. In this category I would include the parthenogenetic tendencies of the Beltsville Small White Turkey. Olsen (1966, 1967, 1968) has shown that about 40% of unfertilized eggs of this strain undergo some development if incubated. Viable young have been hatched, but because in birds the females are the heterogametic sex, the eggs with a YY constitution do not develop; the parthenogenetic poults are invariaby males. The process is a self-defeating one, producing only males. (These could of course mate with their mothers to produce further females [as happens in some Hymenoptera]).

On a taxonomic basis, parthenogenesis as a *regular* feature uncomplicated by by polyploidy or aneuploidy, occurs in many of the fresh-water, terrestrial and a few of the zoo- and phyto-parasitic members of the taxa Hyman (1955) placed in the 'Aschelminthes' (viz. rotifers, nematodes, gastrotrichs) and the tardigrades— all animals which exhibit eutely or constancy of somatic cell number. Amongst terrestrial and fresh water oligochaetes parthenogenesis is very commonly associated with varying degrees of polyploidy (e.g. Muldahl, 1952). The gastropods show regular parthenogenesis in only two fresh water genera of which the New Zealand species *Potamopyrgus antipodarum* is best known (Winterbourn, 1970), and is now widespread in western Europe where it is best known as *P. jenkinsi.*

Otherwise it is only amongst the terrestrial and fresh water Arthropods that parthenogenesis achieves any importance, being well known amongst the Crustacea, Insecta and Acarina. Parthenogenesis is very widespread amongst the fresh water crustaceans (e.g. Branchiopoda and Ostracoda) and also in insects and mites which live in habitats which are spatially and temporally discontinuous.

The occurrence of regular parthenogenesis in the chordate line may be more interesting than important. It is known to occur regularly in very limited numbers of fishes, amphibians and reptiles, extraordinarily rarely in birds, and apparently not at all in mammals. Most vertebrate examples are associated with either pseudogamy or polyploidy or both (Schultz, 1971; Uzzell, 1964; Darevsky, 1966; Maslin, 1971; Olsen, 1966).

Further examination of the distribution of parthenogenesis shows that it is commonly associated with one or more of the factors listed below, which may in themselves be inter-associated:

1. Environmental instability and the exploitation of temporary resources.

2. The absence of regenerative reproduction.

3. The absence of hermaphroditism.

4. Reduced motility of females.

5. Infrequency of males either through genetic drift or low fitness.

6. Polyploidy, aneuploidy, male haploidy.

7. Polymorphism involving neoteny.

8. Discontinuous habitats.

9. Colonising habits.
10. Short generation times.
11. Small somatic size.

For practical purposes parthenogenesis uncomplicated by polyploidy is only common in two phyla, the Aschelminthes and the Arthropoda, and even in these groups it is largely restricted to ephemeral habitats.

PARTHENOGENESIS AND THE GENERATION OF NUMBERS

Clearly parthenogenesis is associated with reproduction in the sense of generation of numbers, but it is noteworthy that where there are alternative non-sexual means of increasing numbers such as budding, fission, etc., as in many marine groups (e.g. Coelenterata, Platyhelminths, Nemerteans, Bryozoans, Polychaetes, Ascidians, Salps) parthenogenesis is virtually unknown. In fresh waters, hydras, bryozoans, sponges and a few oligochaetes (e.g. *Lumbriculus variegatus*) which reproduce regeneratively do not show parthenogenesis. When because of eutely (the Aschelminthes) or apparently because of inconvenient exoskeletons (Arthropoda, Mollusca), regenerative reproduction is not available as an alternative to ovic reproduction, parthenogenesis may be the only available means of rapidly increasing the population. For colonizing species, great advantage lies in the capacity to increase numbers rapidly from an initial population of one. In gonochorists and cross-fertilizing hermaphrodites reproduction time may be wasted in waiting or searching for a mate, which may never be found (Tomlinson, 1966). Similarly when the sex ratio is about 1 : 1 about half the resources of the environment are diverted to the production of males. Assuming that sexual and parthenogenetic forms produce similar numbers of eggs, and that development times are similar, the rate of increase will be much greater in the parthenogenetic species. Thus for a given species the parthenogenetic population will grow at a high rate which should not be distinguishably different from that of a self fertilizing hermaphroditic form, and only slightly greater than an outcrossing hermaphrodite. The diminished performance of the outcrossing hermaphrodite results from time lost in mate-finding and mating.

Reliable data on comparative rates of reproduction in parthenogenetic and gonochoristic forms are hard to find and commonly relate to different stages of population growth and states of development or decline of the habitat. Stalker (1956) found that about 9% of the eggs of *Lonchoptera dubia* did not undergo any development, and that genetically lethal homozygotes occur in the chromosome races of this species. His earlier work (Stalker 1954) had shown that in *Drosophila parthenogenetica* the proportion of eggs undergoing development is variable and presumed to be under polygenic control. On the other hand species which are fully parthenogenetic, at least in some form, as in many nematodes, show no differences in fecundity and viability of the eggs. In his paper on Canadian chrysomelid beetles Robertson (1966) remarked that the parthenogenetic species seemed to show no advantage over the gonochoristic species. Perhaps this is simply a reminder that fecundity is but a single aspect of a species' biology.

On the other hand it is useful to remember that in comparing gonochorism with parthenogenesis one is not strictly comparing the comparable for gonochorism is concerned with more than generation of numbers. Sex is a system for promoting gene flow and the generation of new genetic combinations. A number of secondary features have been added to sex by a sort of evolutionary accretion. Such accretions include sex as a 'social glue', the care of the young, defence of territory and possibly population regulation as envisaged by Wynne Edwards (1962). Of all accretions the imposition of a programmed halt on the development of the unfertilized egg has been most important as a mechanism involved in facilitating the evolution of breeding seasons in iteroparous forms. Eggs which need to be fertilized can be accumulated internally against the breeding season. Eggs which develop without fertilization may give rise to young which kill the mother from within (endotokia matricida) as is common enough in nematodes. It is one of the curiosities of cyclical parthenogenesis that the chief role of the sexual phase seems to be the production of a 'resting' over-wintering, or diapausing egg. In such forms the very small number of progeny produced sexually is to be contrasted with non-sexual generation of numbers (cf. aphids, daphnia, hydra). Just how common is the production of 'resting' disseminules by parthenogenesis is hard to assess from the literature. At least one strain of *Daphnia pulex* can produce ephippial eggs parthenogenetically, and there is good circumstantial evidence for this in the parthenogenetic strains of *Artemia salina*. The production of diapausing stages of *Daphnia* may be wholly a photoperiodic response (Stross, 1968, 1971).

The production of the sexuales in aphids may be a photoperiod phenomenon as in *Megoura viciae* (Lees, 1959) but Gilbert (1968) showed convincingly that the production of a sexual generation in the monogonont rotifer *Asplanchna brightwelli* is dependent upon the ingestion of dietary alpha-tocopherols.

In cyclical parthenogenesis sexual reproduction with its capacity for altering the genotype through recombination typically occurs when the population is at its peak, or just beginning to decline. This timing has several interesting consequences. Firstly mate finding is facilitated by maximal density when the progeny of initially isolated fundatrices may have dispersed and intermingled thus promoting genetic mixing. Secondly, because the eggs produced by the sexual generation commonly enter a quiescent phase the active population rapidly declines. Thirdly we see the relevance of sexual recombination in producing a range of new genotypes immediately before a change of habitats. Once one of these disseminules is activated in a suitable habitat and succeeds in producing a viable adult, time and resources are not wasted in producing a variety of genetic models (sexually); a multitude of replicates of a proven form is produced instead.

PARTHENOGENESIS AND MATE FINDING

Because of the penchant of parthenogenetic species for life in ephemeral habitats, colonization of new habitats is a continuing process. These populations are often reduced to very low numbers; an event which may have several consequences. Such low populations provide ideal conditions for the operation of Sewall Wright's genetic drift or genetic sampling error. As a result males may be eliminated, or may become very rare. Such circumstances favour any tactic which makes males non-essential, and may predispose to selection for hermaphroditism, parthenogenesis, pseudogamy or other secondary multiplicative device such as polyembryony, the sporocyst and redia stages in digenetic trematodes, or multilocular cysts in some taenioid cestodes. The pseudogamous behaviour of the silver crucian carp (*Carassius auratus gibelio*) in Eastern Europe may have had some such origin. In these parts males are rare or unknown and sperm from other fishes (*Carassius carassius, C. auratus auratus* and *Cyprinus carpio*) are used to stimulate development of the eggs (Leider, 1955, 1959).

Very small somatic size, the adoption of sedentary habits, or ones in which there is limited movement of one or both sexes, predisposes to hermaphroditism in many groups, to parthenogenesis in some, and to extraordinary devices to promote insemination of the females in others. Many marine organisms, but very few fresh water species, use motile gametes as substitutes for motile adults. The non-use of free-swimming sperm in fresh water animals is undoubtedly related to the spermicidal properties of fresh water (Leeuwenhoek, 1678).

Where mobility is low (e.g. coccids amongst the Hemiptera, psychids amongst the Lepidoptera, and cecidomyids amongst the Diptera) there seems to be a predisposition towards parthenogenesis. In certain groups hermaphroditism does not seem to be freely available as a device for enhancing effective breeding population size and for reducing the mate-finding problem. Simultaneous functional hermaphroditism does not occur above the fishes in the chordate line, probably because hermaphroditism is not compatible with higher chordate endocrinology. Similar considerations may be involved in the advanced arthropods where hermaphroditism is rare—the scale insect *Icerya purchasi,* and the Termitoxeniidae (Diptera) constitute the only known hermaphroditic insects.

A somewhat different argument has been advanced to account for the absence of males in many Chironomidae (Diptera) and the Coccoidea. This argument is based on coccid males which do not feed after the second nymphal stage, and are particularly frail, weak insects. This leads to a shortage of males and confers great selective advantage on parthenogenetic capacity (Hughes-Schrader, 1948; Nur, 1971).

PARTHENOGENESIS AND POLYPLOIDY

Polyploidy is more common amongst animals than is generally recognised but it is still very much rarer than in plants. Amongst animals departures from the normal diploid state are usually associated with hermaphroditism or parthenogenesis. The reasons for this are to be sought in the chromosomal sex determining mechanism, and in the meiotic processes. It is not surprising that polyploids and aneuploids often show different phenotypes from their diploid ancestors. As Lindroth (1954) has shown the tetraploid parthenogenetic form of *Otiorhynchus dubius* from Scandinavia has a lower thermal limit to its activity which is 2°C lower than for the diploid gonochoristic form from the Alps. Vandel (1928) claimed that the polyploid parthenogenetic form of the land isopod *Trichoniscus elizabethae* is much more drought tolerant than the diploid gonochoristic form. In a similar vein it has been reported that polyploid freshwater crustaceans survive lower oxygen tensions than the normal diploid forms. A further feature of polyploids is the not uncommon capacity to reach maturity in less than normal time.

The clover cyst nematode *Heterodera trifolii* is apparently a triploid ($3n = 27$) parthenogenetic form of the sugar beet nematode *H. scachtii* ($2n = 18$) from which it differs in host range, ploidy, and the sequence of colour changes during cyst formation (Mulvey, 1959). Properties such as these are potentially of adaptive value and no doubt explain in part the much greater geographic range of parthenogenetic forms over gonochoristic forms. The potential capacity of a single parthenogenetic disseminule to establish a new population is of obvious significance. The spread of parthenogenetic New Zealand phasmids into Britain (Uvarov 1944, 1950) and of the New Zealand gastropod *Potamopyrgus antipodarum* into Western Europe is comparable with the great spread of exotic parthenogenetic weevils into North and South America and into Australia (Chadwick, 1970 and Lindroth, 1957). The spread of the fungus beetle *Cis fuscipes* is another recently documented example (Lawrence, 1967).

Parthenogenesis apparently serves as a solution to the cytological problems of polyploidy.

PARTHENOGENESIS, POLYMORPHISM AND PAEDOGENESIS

The potential capacity of parthenogenesis for maximising the rate of increase of a population arises from several sources. These include the obvious ones like the elimination of the non-productive male sex, and the time lag between maturity and fertilization while mates are found and pair bonds established. As Cole (1954) pointed out the time of first reproduction is a matter of great importance in determining the intrinsic rate of increase of a population. If the generation time can be reduced even slightly the effect on population growth can be tremendous (see Lewontin 1965). Thus it is a matter of great practical importance to appreciate that parthenogenesis can accelerate the growth of the population. This capacity can be enhanced by neoteny or paedogenesis—reproduction in a juvenile state. Because there is no requirement for external genitalia, only for the production of eggs which will undergo development without fertilization, the generation time may be reduced. Zaffagnini (1964) has described this process in the polyphemid crustacean (Cladocera) *Bythotrephes longimanus*. Wyatt (1961, 1963, 1967) in a series of papers on fungal feeding Cecidomyiidae has shown how these midges can reduce the generation time, and time to first reproduction, by parthenogenetic paedogenesis. The extent to which the life history (typically egg, three larval instars, pupa, and imago) may be reduced varies, but may be extreme as when the life history consists of a single viviparous parthenogenetic, larval stage. These economies in time and materials are probably important in the exploitation of the evanescent habitat of these flies—the decomposing cambial layer of dead twigs. By eliminating pupal and adult stages no time or energy is wasted on overt adaptation to irrelevant conditions. Reproduction occurs in half the time taken for a full cycle, while fecundity may be reduced to about one third. There are of course no useless males until winged sexual stages are produced again when the habitat becomes unfavourable.

CONCLUSION

The older published literature on parthenogenesis has been dominated by geneticists and cytologists, and contains much that is uncritical and assertive about the 'evolutionary blind alley' that parthenogenesis was seen to represent. At present there is too little knowledge of many aspects of parthenognesis for its evolutionary consequences even to be guessed at. 'Here and now' it is a useful adaptation promoting survival, at least in the short term, by providing immediate substitutes for other reproductive stratagems which, because of previous evolutionary 'decisions' are no longer available.

In placing much reliance on this method of reproduction an organism may be prejudicing future evolutionary plasticity, but even this is not certain—for the obligately parthenogenetic bdelloid rotifers and chaetonotid gastrotrichs probably speciated after becoming parthenogenetic. It could be that parthenogenesis is simply a response to a lack of plasticity elsewhere.

Organisms which show cyclical parthenogenesis such as aphids, cladocerans and monogonont rotifers appear to enjoy the best of all worlds: parthenogenetic reproduction when colonies are being founded and when maximal population growth is likely to result in maximal use of resources. Great increases in numbers serve not only to offset the chances of extinction, but also to enhance the prospects of mate finding and the promotion of genetic interchange when the sexual morph is elicited, usually by environmental stimuli at about the time of maximal density, and just before the population declines.

In this essay much has been made of the ephemeral, fluctuating, and wholly unstable nature of the habitats in which the typically very small, short lived parthenogenetic animals are typically to be found. An alternative view is that these are truly durable, widely distributed and constantly recurring kinds of habitats, and that their inhabitants, the professional colonists of the animal kingdom are already 'living fossils' that remain remarkably well-adapted and ubiquitous. They remain well-adapted because of the lack of change both in themselves and in their habitats. In many respects the parthenogenetic Metazoa are to be compared with many soil Protozoa which also exhibit no sexual process, but are cosmopolitan in distribution, abundant in numbers, and apparently a very old, but successful group.

REFERENCES

Asher, J. H. 1970. Parthenogenesis and genetic variability. II. One locus models for various diploid populations. *Genetics* 66: 369-391.

Asher, J. A. and Nace, G. W. 1971. The genetic structure and evolutionary fate of parthenogenetic amphibian populations as determined by Markovian analysis. *Amer. Zool.* 11: 381-398.

Bodmer, W. F. 1970. The evolutionary significance of recombination in prokaryotes. pp. 279-294. In *Organization and Control in Prokaryotic and Eukaryotic Cells.* 20th Symposium of the Society for General Microbiology. Cambridge Univ. Press.

Brown, S. W. and Bennett, F. D. 1957. On sex determination in the diaspidine scale *Pseudaulacaspis pentagona* (Targ.) (Coccoidea). *Genetics* 42: 510-523.

Bulnheim, H. P. and Vavra, J. 1968. Infection by the microsporidian *Ostosporea effeminans* (Crustacea, Amphipoda). *Verh. dt. zool. Ges.* 1968: 244-260.

Bulnheir, H. P. and Vavra, J. 1968. Infection by the microsporidian *Ostosporea effeminans* sp. n. and its sex determining influence in the amphipod *Gammarus deubeni. J. Parasit.* 54: 241-248.

Carson, H. L. 1967. Permanent heterozygosity. *Evol. Biol.* 1: 143-168.

Caullery, M. and Mesnil, F. 1898. Les formes épitoques et l'evolution des Cirratuliens. *Ann. Univ. Lyon Sci. Nat.* 39: 1-200.

Chadwick, C. E. 1970. South American weevils (Col. Curculionidae) established in Australia. *Aust. J. Sci.* 32: 293-294.

Cole, L. J. 1954. The population consequences of life history phenomena. *Quart. Rev. Biol.* 29: 103-137.

Darevsky, I. S. 1966. Natural parthenogenesis in a polymorphic group of Caucasian rock lizards related to *Lacerta saxicola* Eversmann. *J. Ohio Herpetol. Soc.* 5: 115-152.

Darlington, C. D. 1937. *Recent advances in cytology*. 2nd Ed. Churchill, London.

Downes, J. A. 1965. Adaptations of insects in the Arctic. *A. Rev Ent.* 10: 257-274.

Eshel, I. and Feldman, M. W. 1970. On the evolutionary effect of recombination. *Theoret. Pop. Biol.* 1: 88-100.

Gilbert, J. J. 1968. Dietary control of sexuality in the rotifer *Asplanchna brightwelli* Gosse. *Physiol. Zool.* 41: 14-43.

Hartl, D. L. 1971. Some aspects of natural selection in arrhenotokous populations. *Amer. Zool.* 11: 309-325.

Hartl, D. L. and Brown, S. W. 1970. The origin of male haploid genetic systems and their expected sex ratio. *Theoret. Pop. Biol.* 1: 165-190.

Hughes-Schrader, S. 1948. Cytology of coccids (Coccoidea-Homoptera) *Adv. Genetics* 2: 127-201.

Hyman, L. H. 1955. *The Invertebrates* III. McGraw-Hill, New York.

Lawrence, J. F. 1967. Biology of the parthenogenetic fungus beetle *Cis fuscipes* Mellié (Coleoptera: Ciidae). *Breviora Mus. Comp. Zool.* 258: 1-14.

Lees, A. D. 1959. The role of photoperiod and temperature in the determination of parthenogenetic and sexual forms in the aphid *Megoura viciae* Buckton. I. The influence of these factors on apterous virginoparae and their progeny. *J. Insect Physiol.* 3: 92-117.

Leider V. 1955. Männchenmangel und naturliche Parthenogenese bei der Silberkarausche *Carassius auratus gibelio* (Vertebrata, Pisces). *Naturwissenschaften* 42: 590.

―――― 1959. Über die Eientwicklung bei Männchenlosen stammen der Silberkarausche *Carassius auratus gibelio* (Bloch) (Vertebrata, Pisces). *Biol. Zentralbl.* 135: 212.

Leeuwenhoek, A. 1678. Observations D. Anthonii Leeuwenhock, de natis é Semini genitalia Animalculis. *Phil. Trans. Roy. Soc. Lond.*, 12: 1040-1043.

Lewontin, R. C. 1965. Selection for colonizing ability. pp. 77-91. In H. G. Baker and G. L. Stebbins (eds.) *The Genetics of Colonizing Species*. Academic Press, New York.

Lindroth, C. H. 1954. Experimentelle Beobachtungen an Parthenogenetischen und bisexuellen *Otiorhynchus dubius* Stroem (Col. Curculionidae). *…Ent. Tidskr. Stockholm.* 75- 111-116.

―――― 1957. *The Faunal Connections between Europe and North America*. Almqvist and Wiksell, Stockholm.

Maslin, T. P. 1971. Parthenogenesis in reptiles. *Amer. Zool.* 11: 361-380.

Mockford, E. L. 1971. Parthenogenesis in psocids (Insecta: Psocoptera). *Amer. Zool.* 11: 327-339.

Muldahl, S. 1952. The chromosomes of earthworms. I The evolution of polyploidy. *Heredity* 6: 58-76.

Mulvey, R. H. 1959. Investigations on the clover cyst nematode, *Heterodera trifolii* (Nematoda: Heteroderidae). *Nematologica* 4: 147-156.

Nur, V. 1971. Parthenogenesis in coccids (Homoptera). *Amer. Zool.* 11: 301-308.

Olliver, J. H. 1971. Parthenogenesis in mites and ticks (Arachnida: Acari). *Amer. Zool.* 11: 283-299.

Olsen, M. W. 1966. Segregation and replication of chromosomes in turkey parthenogenesis. *Nature.* 212: 435-436.

―――― 1967. Age as a factor influencing the level of parthenogenesis in eggs of turkeys. *Proc. Soc. exp. Biol. Med.* 124: 617-619.

―――― 1968. Frequency of three malpositions among full term parthenogenetic turkeys. *Poult. Sci.* 47: 1587-1589.

Olsen, M. W. and Buss, E. G. 1967. Role of genetic factors and fowl pox virus in parthenogenesis in turkey eggs. *Genetics* 56: 727-732.

Robertson, J. G. 1966. The chromosomes of bisexual and parthenogenetic species of *Callignapha* (Coleoptera: Chysomelidae) with notes on sex ratio, abundance and egg number. *Can. J. Genet. Cytol.* 8: 695-732.

Schultz, R. J. 1971. Special adaptive problems associated with unisexual fishes. *Amer. Zool.* 11: 351-360.

Smith, J. M. 1971. What use is sex? *J. Theoret. Biol.* 30: 319-335.

Smith, S. G. 1971. Parthenogenesis and polyploidy in beetles. *Amer. Zool.* 11: 341-349.

Stalker, H. D. 1954. Parthenogenesis in *Drosophila*. *Genetics*, 39: 4-34.

―――― 1956. On the evolution of parthenogenesis in *Lonchoptera* (Diptera). *Evolution*, 10: 345-359.

Stolk, A. 1958. Pathological parthenogenesis in viviparous toothcarps. *Nature* 181: 1600.

Stross, R. G. 1911. Photoperiod control of diapause in *Daphnia*. IV Light and CO_2-sensitive phases within the cycle of activation. *Biol. Bull.* 140: 137-155.

Stross, R. G. and Hill, J. C. 1968. Photoperiod control of winter diapause in the freshwater crustacean, *Daphnia*. *Biol. Bull.* 137: 359-374.

Suomalainen, E. 1950. Parthenogenesis in animals. *Adv. Genetics* 3: 193-253.

———— 1962. Significance of parthenogenesis in the evolution of insects. *A. Rev. Ent.* 7: 349-366.

Tomlinson, J. 1966. The advantages of hermaphroditism and parthenogenesis. *J. Theoret. Biol.* 11: 54-58.

Uvarov, B. P. 1944. A New Zealand phasmid (Orthoptera) established in the British Isles. *Proc. Roy. Ent. Soc. Lond.* (B) 15: 94-96.

———— 1950. A second New Zealand stick-insect (Phasmatodea) established in the British Isles. *Proc. Roy. Ent. Soc. Lond.* (B) 19: 174-175.

Uzzell, T. M. 1964. Relations of the diploid and triploid species of the *Amblystoma jeffersonianum* complex (Amphibia: Caudata). *Copeia* 2: 257-300.

Vandel, A. 1931a. *La Parthenogenese*. G. Doine et Cie, Paris.

———— 1931b. Sur l'existence de deux especes de *Trichoniscus* du sous-genre *Spiloniscus* (Crustaces: Isopodes) jusqu'ici confondues et sur leurs rapports reciproques. *Rendu Acad. Sci. Paris* 193: 752-754.

———— 1933. Liste des especes de Trichoniscidae (Crustaces—Isopodes) signale es jusqu'ici en France comprenant la description de plusirs especes nouvelles. *Arch. Zool. exp. gen.* 75: 35-54.

White, M. J. D. 1948. *Animal Cytology and Evolution*. Cambridge University Press, Cambridge.

———— 1954. *ibid.* Second Edition.

———— 1970. Heterozygosity and genetic polymorphism in parthenogenetic animals. pp. 237-262. In M. K. Hecht and W. C. Steere (eds.). *Essays in Evolution and Genetics in Honour of Theodosius Dobzhansky*. North-Holland Publishing Co., Amsterdam.

Winterbourn, M. J. 1970. The New Zealand species of *Potamopyrgus* (Gastropoda: Hydrobiidae). *Malacologia*, 10: 283-321.

Wyatt, I. J. 1961. Pupal paedogenesis in the Cecidomyiidae (Diptera). *Proc. Roy. Ent. Soc. Lond. (A.)* 36: 133-143.

———— 1963. Pupal paedogenesis in the Cecidomyiidae (Diptera) 2. *Proc. Roy. Ent. Soc. Lond. (A.)* 38: 136-144.

———— 1967. Pupal paedogenesis in the Cecidomyiidae (Diptera) 3. A reclassification of the Heteropezini. *Trans. Roy. Soc. Lond.* 119: 71-98.

Wynne-Edwards, V. C. 1962. *Animal Dispersion in Relation to Social Behaviour*. Oliver and Boyd, Edinburgh.

Zaffagnini, F. 1964. Il ciclo reproduttivo partenogenetico di *Bythotrephes longimanus* Leydig (Cladocera: Polyphemidae). *Revista di Idrobiologia* 3: 97-109.

INDEX

The index is in four parts (a) general, (b) aphid species, (c) aphid pathogens and (d) plant species.

A—GENERAL

Aberrations 106
Absolute time-scale 87
Acarina 106
Actidione 59
Acquisition 92
Adaptation 17, 27, 55, 56, 65
Adelgidae 41, 44
Aerial application 11, 14
Age resistance 25
Ageing 78
Aggregate 76-78, 80, 82, 83
Aggregation 56, 61, 77, 79, 82
Agricultural crops 7, 8, 17, 18, 44, 83
Agroecosystem 98
Agronomist 49
Air masses 98
Aleyrodidae 95
Algebraic solutions 85
Alighting 80
Allele 40
Allylisothiocyanate 58
Alpha-amylase 14
Alpha tocopherols 108
Alternate 45
Ameiotic 103, 104
America 46
Amides 56, 57, 60, 61
Amino acids 55-58, 60, 61, 65, 70, 72
Amphibians 106
Androcyclic 55, 83
Aneuploidy 106, 109
Anholocycly 16, 42, 43, 47, 52, 55, 83
Annual crops 83
Annual ring 61
Antennae 70
Antibiotics 59, 69
Antigens 96
Apex 59
Aphicide 14
Aphid-borne 97-99
Aphid control 8
Aphid hosts 32
Aphididae 45
Aphidiidae 20
Aphids 108, 111
Aphidius smithi 20-27
Aphid-virus problems 7, 8, 11, 13, 17
Aphid warning 8, 10
Approximations 89
Aqueous extracts 70
Arginine 45
Artificial diets 18
Argentina 34

Arrestant 49
Arthropoda 103, 105, 107
Aschelminthes 106, 107
Ascidians 107
Asexual 17, 31, 52, 103, 104
Asparagine 45, 57
Assimilation rate 79
Aster yellows 97
Attached leaves 60
Attraction 54
Aureomycin 69
Australia 16, 89
Avoidance tactics 10, 12, 54
Azygospores 31

Bacteria 30
Baking tests 14
Banvel D 59
Barban 59
Barrier 44
Barley yellow dwarf 8, 13, 18, 98
Bean yellow mosaic 96
Beetles 103
Beet leaf curl 97
Beet mosaic 99
Beet yellow 97, 99
BHC 42, 47
Biological control 13, 17, 47, 98, 99
Biotypes 40-49, 58, 82, 83
Birds 106
Birth rate 15, 17, 85, 90
Bivoltine 45, 97
Blastoderm 58
Blind alley 110
Brachypterous 65, 66
Brachiopoda 105
Branchiopoda 106
Breeding, plant 8
Britain 110
Bryozoans 107
Budding 104, 107
Budgets 85-87, 90
Butterflies 44
Build-up 17

C14 79
Cage 77
California 42
Cambium 61, 110
Campbell Islands 16
Carbamate 47
Carbon dioxide 79
Carp 108
Carrot motley dwarf 10, 18
Cauliflower mosaic 18

114

Phenylalanine 57
Phloem 56, 58, 60, 69, 72
Phoresy 20
Phosphate 71
Photoperiod 52, 65, 72, 73, 96, 108
Photosynthate 79
Photosynthesis 79
Phycomycetes 31
Physiology 56-59
Phytochemical 55, 68, 70-73, 80, 81, 87, 88,
　　　　　　　　93-97
Phytophagous 41, 49
Phytosterols 58
Pigment 40
Piesmidae 94
Plant age 59, 60
Plant breeders 13, 46-49
Plant tissue 56, 93
Planting date 11, 98, 99
Plague 16
Plasticity 41, 111
Platyhelminths 107
Polychaete 105
Polyembryony 108
Polygenic 107
Polyhedral 96
Polymorphism 46, 52, 62, 65-73, 87, 106, 110
Polyphagous 42, 44, 45, 55, 72
Polyploidy 106-110
Population 13-15, 30, 31, 41-49, 55, 61, 76-83,
　　　　　　　　85-91, 98, 99, 103-111
Population density 13, 14, 88
Population survival 27
Population theory 85
Population trends 88, 89
Populations, parellel 16
Post-natal development 68, 73
Potato leaf roll 10, 18, 97, 99
Potato X, Y 10, 18, 92, 98
Predator 11, 13, 15, 17, 18, 47, 55, 78, 82,
　　　　　　　　89, 90, 99
Predictions 57, 58, 85
Preference 22, 23, 26, 43-45, 54, 68, 72
Preferred host 16
Pre-natal development 68, 73
Pressures 44
Pressurised diet 56
Preventive 10
Primary host 45, 47
Primary infection 98
Primary species (aphids) 12
Primitive 45
Primordium 105
Probing 54, 55, 69, 70, 92, 105
Proboscis 33, 34
Progenitors 46
Progeny 40, 44, 48, 49, 66, 68, 73, 76-78, 81,
　　　　　　　　108
Proline 57, 67, 68
Propagative 92
Protein 14, 73
Protozoa 111
Pseudogamy 104-106, 108

Psocoptera 103
Psychids 109
Psyllids 4, 46
Psyllidae 94

Quantitative studies 18
Quip 87

Races 40-43, 97
Radiotracer 54
Rainfall 31
Random variation 86
Range 44, 46, 48, 55, 72, 85, 109
Raspberry mosaic 99
Receptors 55
Red leaf virus 12, 13, 18
Redia stage 108
Regenerative reproduction 103-107
Regressions 57
Regurgitate 93
Reinfestation 14
Reproduction 103-104
Reproductive barriers 41
Reproductive rate 77, 81, 107, 110
Reproductive stage 17
Reptiles 106
Reserve hosts 45
Resistance 28, 40, 42-49, 57-60, 98, 99
Resistant plants 8, 10, 17, 18
Respiration 61
Responses 73
Resting spores 32, 33
Restlessness 66, 80
Retention 92, 93
Reverin 59
Revised concepts 15
Rhizoids 31-33
Ribose 56
Rickettsiaceae 58, 92
Roots 59, 61
Rotifers 103, 106, 108, 111
"Runts" 80

Saliva 61
Salivary glands 92
Salps 107
Samples 85, 88
Sap 58, 59, 69
Sap-feeding 55, 56, 86
Scalar 87
Scale insects 103, 109
Scandinavia 109
Secondary host 45
Secondary spread 8, 98
Secondary substances 55, 57
Seed crop 17, 99
Seed infected 99
Seed set 14
Seed treatment 98
Seedlings 70, 71
Selection 8, 20, 44, 54, 59, 76, 77, 83
Self-regulation 81-83
Semi-persistent 93, 98

119

Viability 107
Villose conidia 33
Viral pathogens 30
Viremia 96
Virus 18, 41-43, 47, 48, 92, 93, 96, 99, 105
Virus classification 93, 96
Virus damage 8
Virus-free seed 11
Virus spread 11
Viruses, list of 94-95
Viscosity 55
Vitamins 68, 71
Volatile components 70
Voltage variations 54

Warning, see aphid warning
Washington 99
Water 54-56, 59
Waxy surface 70

Weather 31, 43, 48
Weeds 7, 98
Weevil 30
Wilting 59, 61
Wind 16, 44
Wing muscles 73
Wing production 65, 69
Wintering 96, 99
Wounding 57

Xylem 61

"Yellows" diseases 92
Yield 11, 14

Zinc, see Zn
Zn 66
Zygospores 31, 32

B—APHID SPECIES

Acyrthosiphon dirhodum 35
    festucae 42
    malvae 42
    perlargonii 42
    pisum 20-26, 30, 32, 34-36,
      41, 42, 45, 46, 58, 59, 70-72,
          77, 83, 99
    solani 11, 12, 18, 32, 33, 36,
      37, 42
    spartii 21
Amphoraphora rubi 42, 45, 46
Aphis craccae 32, 34
   craccivora 12, 42, 59, 89, 98
   fabae 32-37, 42, 45, 54, 59, 61, 72, 77,
            78, 80-83
   farinosa 71
   forbesi 32, 36
   gossypii 31, 35-37, 42, 47, 57, 59
   ilicis 35
   nasturtii 32, 33, 36, 42
   nerii 37
   pomi 32, 34, 70
   rumicis 32
   sambuci 32, 35, 79
   spiraecola 35

Betulaphis quadrituberculata 36
Brachycaudus helichrysi 7, 12, 32, 35
Brachycolus asparagi 32
Brevicoryne brassicae 8, 12-14, 17, 18, 21,
    32, 33, 37, 42, 45, 54-61, 70,
        76-80, 85, 87-90

Capitophorus elaeagni 12
    hippohaes 32
Cavariella aegopodii 7, 12, 16, 18, 35, 37, 42
    pastinaceae 32, 35
    theobaldi 35
Chaetosiphon fragaefolii 35, 42, 47, 65

Chromaphis juglandicola 42, 47
Coloradoa rufomaculata 31
Cryptomyzus galeopsidis 42

Dactynotus ambrosiae 73
    cichorii 21
     taraxaci 34
Drepanosiphum dixoni 65
    platanoidis 35, 61, 76, 82
Dysaphis anthrisci 42
    devecta 61, 71
    majkopica 42
    plantaginea 35, 47, 72
    pyri 47

Eriosoma lanigerum 42
    pyricola 62
Euceraphis betulae 35
    punctipennis 36
Eucallipterus tiliae 61, 83

Hyadaphis erysimi 31
Hyalopterous pruni 54, 79

Liosomaphis berberidis 35
Lipaphis erysimi 12, 42, 56
    pseudobrassicae 60

Macrosiphoniella sanborni 31
    tanacetaria 32
Mascrosiphum avenae 14, 35, 45, 48, 59
    euphorbiae 12-15, 18, 31-33,
          35, 36, 42, 47
    miscanthi 11, 14, 16-18, 45
    rosae 14, 21, 32, 35, 37, 43,
          58
Megoura viciae 21, 33, 36, 37, 43, 59, 108
Metopolophium 42
Microlophium evansi 21, 32, 35, 36

121

Myzocallis asclepiadis 46
Myzodium modestum 37
Myzus cerasi 47
ornatus 37
persicae 11-13, 16, 18, 21, 22, 31,
33-36, 43, 45, 47, 48, 54-
61, 65-67, 69-71, 76, 83,
98, 99

Nasonovia lactucae 32, 35, 36
lampsanae 32
Neomyzus circumflexus 47

Pemiphigus bursarius 32
Phorodon humuli 43, 47, 72
Phylloxera vastatrix 43

Rhodobium porosum 47
Rhopalomyzus lonicerae 32, 36

Rhopalosiphoninus staphyleae 32, 36
Rhopalosiphum fitchii 34
insertum 35, 43, 70
maidis 32, 60
padi 8, 12-14, 16, 18, 32, 35,
43, 59, 71, 72

Schizaphis graminum 36, 43, 46, 54, 58, 59
Schizolachnus piniradiatae 32, 34

Therioaphis trifolii 30, 43, 47, 60
maculata 33, 34, 37, 43, 47
Toxoptera aurantii 31, 43

Viteus vitifoliae 43

C—APHID PATHOGENS

Acrostalagmus aphidum 31

Boudierella coronata 32
Bacillus thuringiensis 30

Cladiosporium aphidis 30
Cephalosporium aphidicola 30
muscarium 30
Conidiobolus villosus 32

Delacroixia coronata 32

Empusa see Entomopthora
lageniformis 34
radians 36
Entomophthora aphidis 31-33, 37
atrosperma 32
chromaphidis 35
coronata 32, 35, 37
destruens 37
exitialis 33
ferruginea 35
fresenii 33, 34
ignobilis 36

lageniformis 34
neri 37
obscura 34, 35
occidentalis 34
phytonomi 36
planchoniana 15, 35-37
pyriformis 35
sphaerosperma 35-37
thaxteriana 35-37
virulenta 35-37

Hirsutella aphidis 30

Neozygites aphidis 33

Paecilomyces farinosus 30

Spicaria, see Paecilomyces

Tarichium aphidis 32
sphaerospermum 36
Triplosporium fresenii 33
lageniformis 34

D—PLANT SPECIES

Alfalfa 43, 60
Apple 42, 71
Asclepia 46
Asclepiadaceae 46
Avena sativa 21

Barley 58, 60
Bean 59, 71, 72, 78, 83
Beet 54, 97, 99
Betula populifoliae 34, 35,

Betulaceae 45
Birch 35
Brassicas 8, 60, 76
Brassica oleracea gemmifera 76
Broad bean 21, 22
Broom 21
Brussels Sprouts 54, 56, 58-61, 76, 79

Cabbage 54, 79, 80
Calla 42